Three Billion Years
of Life

Three Billion Years of Life

ANDRE DE CAYEUX

Translated from the French by
JOYCE E. CLEMOW

Stein and Day / *Publishers* / New York

Published simultaneously in Canada by Saunders of Toronto, Ltd.
Designed by Bernard Schleifer
Printed in the United States of America

Stein and Day/*Publishers*/7 East 48 Street, New York, N.Y. 10017

Contents

Preface

1

Terrestrial Evolution, A Cosmic Phenomenon

1

The Hebrew patriarch who believed himself promised a lineage as numerous as the stars in the sky wisely did not attempt to count them, but placed his trust in the Almighty. On a clear moonless night, the eye never sees more than two to three thousand stars. But, toward the end of the eighteenth century, the elder Herschel constructed the first giant telescope; and the sight he saw made him dizzy. The Milky Way, this faintly luminous band of stars stretching around the sky, enhanced by some anthropomorphic legend in every folklore of this earth—the pilgrim route, milk spread over the celestial canopy—the Milky Way was a stream of stars.

Now, two centuries later, we know that these stars, numbering around two hundred billion are, in fact, all suns. We also know that the immense galactic universe (which light takes several hundreds of thousands of years to cross at a speed of 186,000 miles a second) is only one among the billions of universes revealed through long-exposure photos from the great telescopes and through radio astronomy. Perhaps there is even an infinite number of these universes in a boundless space that is endlessly strewn with stars. But let us consider, in our universe, this Milky Way that encircles our sky like a colossal smoke ring.

Astrophysicists have observed that all the suns forming it rotate on their axes like tops: some make a complete rotation in a few days or even a few hours; others spin slowly, taking several weeks to rotate once. Our sun, for example, rotates once in twenty-five days, as any-

7

one can verify by projecting its image onto a piece of white paper through a lens, and by following the displacement of the shadow from one edge of the disk to the other. Why is the rotation time of the stars not more or less identical? Simply because the suns that rotate slowly, like our sun, have planets. Something has reduced a part of the kinetic rotation energy in the central star, and this something is the planets, which not only rotate on their axes but also revolve around the sun in their annual revolution. Van de Kamp, Schlesinger, and some others have, in effect, shown by direct method that a large proportion of the suns close to ours have planets, and that, like our sun, these suns rotate slowly.

This fact is then clear: the stars rotating slowly are stars with planets, and these are very numerous. They number at least one out of ten, and maybe one out of three or four. So, there are most likely several tens of billions of planetary systems in our galactic system. Once we become aware of this fantastic reality, it is hard to stop thinking about it. Earth is everything for us. Our whole history has unfolded on its soil as well as the infinitely longer history of the life that created us. Consequently, if earth is destined to remain our sole homeland, it is frightening to discover its minute place in the entirety of the universe.

All the efforts men have made appear insignificant. First there was their long struggle against animals throughout prehistory, then their struggle against misery, hunger, ignorance, and disease from the earliest civilizations on. So much work, tears, and blood, so much meditation and, in short, so much love, so many mothers bending over their children, so many heroes, and even so many people have been sacrificed in the name of progress of a more just or truer idea. All of these things would have no more place in the heart of a monstrously vast universe than one drop of water in the breaking wave. For we can make the reckoning if we like: the image of the sky as revealed by astronomy in the last fifty years reduces us to the size of a grain of dust. Consequently, it is easy to understand the desperate pessimism professed by Jean Rostand in *Les Pensées d'un biologiste (Thoughts of a Biologist)*. Seen thus, man, in effect, is nothing but a shadow laden with burdens and pain. His brief existence is an absurd and sinister farce; and his awareness of it, if it does not add to his nobleness as Pascal asserts, intensifies all the more the fruitlessness of his torment. What is the point of my working on or caring for the truth of the lines I write at the cost of a life of burden if not only my life but all life is definitely consecrated to cosmic annihilation with the predicted the end of the planet? One day, the Parthenon, the Sainte-Chapelle, the Great Pyramid, the last reproduction of the "Mona Lisa" and the last copy of Gargantua's adventures will be reduced to dust. If none of all that will eventually remain, why even have undertaken it?

Such are the thoughts that have beset so many enlightened men for the last two centuries, ever since those icy-cold nights in the Age of Enlightenment when, under the stars, Herschel was dictating the first results of his celestial explorations to his sister Caroline. After many millennia of anthropocentric pride, when our ancestors worshiped the creator of the universe in the form of the little Jupiter of their tribe, the telescope has suddenly revealed that the sky is boundless. The little Jupiters shiver ridiculously in their frozen spaces, and pride gives way to despair. But we believe that this despair is as misplaced as this pride and that it stems from the same spiritual weakness. It is our belief that the minds who now proclaim the downfall of man under the pretext that he is no longer the central point of the world are the same men who used to enforce worship of the little shivering Jupiters by means of tribunals and burning at the stake.

One must be terribly lacking in ambition and imagination to regret being born into the world as a human being. And one must have lost all spirit of youth not to have wanted our species to have evolved as it has. Thank heavens (and that is the right word to use!), we are brought back to reality as soon as we make the effort to study it.

For we see the facts as they are. There are billions of planets in the sky revolving around stars of all types and all ages. We certainly still have the night to believe that of all these planets only one has pushed its biological evolution as far as rational intelligence, even though our sun is like a twin to billions of these stars with planets. (In passing, we must note that we no longer have the right to believe that life exists only on earth. Astronomers now know that life also exists on Mars.) To imagine that earth alone has produced its sphere of understanding, its thinking species, is the last refuge of petty tribal

pride. We can still comfort ourselves with this infantile illusion for
some time yet: until man has completely mastered astronautical
techniques, at the latest by the end of the century. For our part, from
the successive collapse of all anthropocentric dreaming since Coper-
nicus, we must draw the following conclusion: just as the sun is a
star among many stars, so the earth is a planet among many planets,
and terrestrial understanding is only one of many understandings.
Man is only one among the countless thinking species populating the
universe. His solitude is as momentary as were all the periods of his
history and prehistory. Although some men of the Cro-Magnon race
were able to believe that nothing existed beyond the banks of the
Dordogne, we refuse to intensify their error by believing that nothing
exists beyond the confines of our present universe.

So we are living in the last years of terrestrial solitude. As André
de Cayeux says, a period of planetary history that has lasted for
thirty or thirty-five million centuries is ending. This means that the
few decades separating us from our first contact with extraterrestrial
life and perhaps extraterrestrial thought have something sacred about
them and that humanity should live them in peaceful contemplation
and exaltation, gathering together the noblest, most beautiful, and
greatest results of its long labor. And in this peaceful contemplation,
there could be no timelier meditation than the one suggested to us
by the history of terrestrial life. For just as the study of an alfalfa
cell or a slug's cell enlightens us about the human cell, so certain
biological facts discovered by science are common to all forms of
terrestrial life. And likewise, terrestrial life, in its individuality, must
illustrate in its own way the cosmic universal laws that are valid for
every biosphere scattered throughout the sidereal system.

To a certain extent, it is universal life, the life of the most distant
planets that we observe in a forest, a field, or a crowd. From this, we
have gained a sort of intuition. From the time of Omar Khayyam,
since the *Song of Songs* and Gilgamesh, poetic musing has spontaneously associated love, the aroma of a garden at night, and the
twinkling of the stars. But science can justify this ingenuous association. Everything we know about the fundamentals of biology—from
the most recent works on ribonic and desoxyribonucleic acids, on
protein molecules, and on what we could call microgenetics, the
patient decoding of the most intimate architecture of the smallest and

simplest cells, their nutritive and reproductive mechanisms—everything seems to indicate that life is first and foremost a superior game of chemistry, of crystal, and of electronics (in time, by order of historical appearance, and in space, by its infinitesimal organization). In short, it is a laborious production of the fundamental principles of physics. Indeed, as Brillouin, Ruyer, and especially Olivier Costa de Beauregard have shown, physics is no longer the brutal mechanical system of Auguste Compte's and Marcelin Berthelot's time, with all due respect to certain biologists who obstinately cling to a doctrine of physics refuted by physicists for thirty years. But it is now more definite than it ever was before, that life is an activity *based on laws that are identical from one end of the universe to the other.*

When we analyze the spectrum of the most distant stars, we find the same hydrogen, iron, oxygen, nitrogen, and sodium rays. This implies an identical architecture of the atoms of these different bodies, and consequently, a chemistry that is none other than terrestrial chemistry, on which the whole structure of terrestrial life rests, even down to our thought itself. Once again, this is in no way a partisan or materialistic interpretation of life or thought since physics itself has ceased being materialistic, using the word in the sense it had before the cyberneticians reinterpreted it thermodynamically. And once again, mention should be made of that extaordinary sentence written by Costa de Beauregard in his last book: [1] "It is my conviction that the material universe studied in physics is not the whole universe, but that it masks, proves, and shows a glimpse of another much more primordial universe of a psychic nature, of which the material universe is like a passive and partial counterpart." This statement, note well, written by one of the most eminent present-day physicists, bears witness to the revolution accomplished by physics in the past half-century. Universal life, therefore, is based on properties of matter that are likewise universal and have been made more and more specifically known through physics. But then, the miracle of terrestrial life stops being a miracle. Or rather, instead of ceasing to be a miracle, it is only the local reflection of a greater

[1] *Le second principe de la science du temps,* Paris, 1963.

miracle on the scale of the infinite universe, which is what Costa de Beauregard calls elsewhere the psychic *counterpart* of the physical world. At the core of the atom, even at the core of the fundamental particles and the laws animating them, there is a special something that Teilhard de Chardin felt intuitively was present and that he glorified, and this tends eternally and infallibly toward life and consciousness. It is this something that paleontologists and geologists like André de Cayeux see at work on the earth when they reconstruct the remains that have lain beneath our feet for more than three billion years of life and death.

Three billion years of life represents an incredible number of individuals, adventures, and species that have appeared and disappeared, of evolutions and inventions of all kinds. It has been said that everything that was possible has occurred and that all creatures capable of living exist or have existed. But this statement must be corrected in the light of modern ecological studies: bearing in mind the fact that every appearance of a new species creates fresh conditions, consequently, evolution can continue indefinitely.

In the apparent chaos of living forms that we discover by visiting a botanical garden, a zoo, and a paleontological museum, the first observation that strikes us is that every time there is a possibility of living in a certain way, be it baroque, complicated, or absurd (in our eyes), there also exists one or generally even several creatures exploiting the possibility: *every possible environment is exploited.* It is not sufficient to say that where there is a cabbage, there is always a goat to eat it. Careful study of a cabbage will show that there are scores of living creatures busy living at its expense, from bacteria, fungi, and viruses to slugs and cabbage butterflies, etc. The slug itself will have its parasites, and so will the cabbage butterfly. In the latter insect, the parasites differ for the caterpillar and the butterfly. In addition, the cabbage butterfly is stung by a hymenoptera called *Apanteles glomeratus,* which lays its eggs there. And so on, because the *Apanteles* has its parasites too. Everything exists in nature.

The radiations given off by a radioactive body kill most living creatures. Nowhere since the origin of the earth has there been an environment made up of heavy radiated water. But the Americans observed one day that the water in one of their atomic batteries was strangely muddy. They blocked the battery, examined the water, and

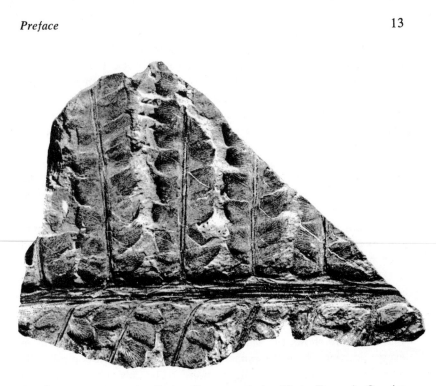

Fossilized fern from the Carboniferous period.—Photo François Garnier

found a bacterial colony there thriving under radiation believed to be fatal to all forms of life. There are living creatures in crude petrol, in the boiling water of geysers, in the solfataras, and in the most un-healthy caves (unhealthy for us, that is). Countless living creatures are born, live, and die in the ball-point pen which wrote these lines, in the paper on which I am writing and the paper which you are reading, in my intestine and in yours. I still remember the burst of laughter from Dr. Salisbury, Professor of Botany at the University of Colorado and a specialist in extraterrestrial life, when I told him how a distinguished professor at the College de France had proved for me one day that life was impossible on Mars.

"Let him name one place on earth," he said to me, "where life does not exist, even if it were in places with conditions one hundred times severer than on the planet Mars."

There are insects which get fat and fornicate inside boxes of insecticides, while others gnaw the copper of electric wires. The Americans have had to throw out as scrap iron billions of dollars worth of intercontinental rockets whose circuits had aroused the appetite of a bacteria. The name of this bacteria, though, has been kept secret, no doubt in the hope that their opponents in space can benefit from it too!

This fury of life to eat everything that is edible and even what is not, to inhabit everything that can be inhabited, to gnaw, nibble, devour, to make elbow-room, wing- and fin-room, to occupy anything that is empty, usurp what is occupied, to kill the rival, imitate him, cut the grass from under his feet and the feet along with it, to out-do him, out-do oneself, and finally to evolve in every possible direction and then more, this is surely the first, fundamental characteristic, as universal and fundamental as the structure of the simple bodies or the structure of spectral rays. We do not know if *Epsilon Eridani,* the sister star of the sun, has planets, or if these hypothetical planets have an atmosphere. But if this biosphere exists, we can rest assured that life there shows the same untiring ingenuity to push forward in every direction, the same capacity for self-renewal, self-control, self-extermination, and self-multiplication, with only one reservation (which we shall come back to soon), that *here is the image of the beginning of life,* corresponding to the first three billion years of terrestrial evolution, related in this book. But we do not know what comes *after*.

There have been many speculations on "different" lives. Science fiction writers and biochemists have visualized living systems based on silicon chemistry, sulfur and selenium chemistries. If these systems are capable of living, then they certainly exist somewhere, perhaps with creatures who speculate on the possibility of a carbon chemistry. But it seems that the differences in basic chemistry have no special philosophical bearing. On earth, one of the most universal characteristics of life is the use of completely dissimilar means for identical ends. In order to move from place to place, an insect called a *gerris* (which is a type of slender water bug) runs on top of the water with its long hydrophobic legs. It uses a physical property of liquid, which can not wet the ends of its limbs. And this procedure works very well for it. Try to catch this sea traveler with a stick or a net and you will see. The gerris runs over the mirror-like liquid with the agility of a skater. But here is the case of another insect, just as nimble as the gerris, moving over the same liquid mirror. It is the *stenus,* studied by Mr. René Baudouin, Professor at the Sorbonne, Paris. Like the gerris, the stenus has hydrophobic legs. But, in order to move, it does not go to the bother of running. Through its anus, it simply discharges a fine, fibrous, tensio-active substance, which, when it comes into contact with water, immediately expands to occupy the largest possible surface. The result is very simple. The stenus is propelled forward like a rocket! In this case there is a propelling reaction; in the preceding case it was simply a matter of running; what could be more different? But the result is the same. The stenus and gerris, by adopting two unrelated physical properties, have acquired the same mobility and have conquered the same environment, where they live side by side like brothers.

The goal to be reached, along with nutrition and reproduction, is perhaps the most general law of life. The mysterious force that has swept living creatures and species along since the birth of the earth apparently has only one concern, the goal to be reached. This in no way signifies, though, that this goal is conscious or understood, or that it even exists. Let us go down beneath the surface colonized by the sea travelers into the very depths of the aquatic habitat. In order to move rapidly in the water, fins are necessary on both sides and at the end of the tail; and to be stabilized, this propeller system in turn requires a vertical dorsal fin. Indeed this system exists or has existed in creatures as diversified as the shark (which is a fish), the ichthyosaurus (which was a reptile), and the dolphin (which is a mammal). These three masterpieces of nature are almost replicas of each other, although they have about as many anatomical similarities as a bleak, a tortoise, and a cow. It all appears as though nature had for a long time taken it into her head to remodel the cow and tortoise, disguising them as fish, or else as though the cow and tortoise could become so pliable (under certain conditions) that they could simply be given to a sculptor to get the shape one wanted from them. What could be more different than a dolphin and a bat? One resembles a fish and the other a bird. Yet they have identical ancestry and stem from identical matter. But the dolphin is adapted for life in water and the bat for life in the air.

Convergence is the name given by naturalists to these similar characteristics that evolved from widely different ancestries but which are analogous responses to identical needs, according to Lucien Cuenot in *L'evolution biologique*. Animals as diversified as the duck, the frog, and the Newfoundland dog all have more or less webbed feet. They are not webbed as a result of the raw material which served to make the animal: in the first case, a type of bird; in the second case, a type of amphibian; in the third case, a type of mammal. They are webbed solely as a result of the environment to which all three are more or less adapted. The webbing of these different feet, which shows striking resemblances, has been realized independently by nature three times. *And it does not matter that we are unsure of the mechanisms resulting in this triple success, nor does it matter whether Lamarck or Darwin or neither is right.* What is important is the fact (proved) that nature is capable of carrying out the same assemblage, almost down to the same creature, from completely different raw materials. In his book André de Cayeux gives several astonishing examples of convergence. Here are some more, which are just as thought-provoking.

Liz Taylor's eyes, an octopus's eyes, and a clam's eyes have an almost identical lens, which in all three cases was obtained by equally effective but completely unrelated means. Let us read Herbert Wendt's description in his book *Les animaux* of the death of an octopus, harpooned during a fishing expedition in the Mediterranean:

"Is the animal suffering? Cephalopoda have an extremely sensitive nervous system, and the movements the imprisoned animal makes to defend itself do not resemble 'conditioned reflexes' at all. Gradually the tentacles approach the wound where the harpoon's teeth penetrated. The fisherman, proud of his exploit, is holding it with a sturdy hand. And suddenly, two large, almost human-looking eyes protrude from the enormous limp head at the end of two thick pads; not only do they seem blinded by the light, but they also express the wounded animal's anguish and suffering and an immense grief. These eyes, so similar to ours, protruding from the body of a mollusk, give us a feeling of uneasiness when we see them for the first time. What does their language mean? We attribute to animals the ability to experience human feelings; yet, powerless, we watch them die. However, structurally, cephalopoda's eyes do have striking similarities to the eyes of vertebrates. Their eyes do not fit in with their sack-shaped heads and their tentacles. The octopus hunting at the bottom of the sea has a look that reminds us of a cat. But when struck to death it convulses in its death throes, it really has a human look about it."

It would be more accurate to say that the human look has some similarities to that of the octopus, because the latter was viewing the marvels of the world under the sea tens of millions of years before the first man appeared. And it is the octopus that would be justified in finding that the fisherman killing it looked strange.

However, it is in studying Australian fauna that naturalists have been able to measure the generality of convergence phenomena. The Australian continent has developed aside from the rest of the world from a period when the most evolved vertebrates were the marsupials. While Europe, Asia, Africa, and North America were witnessing the appearance of placental mammals, which very quickly supplanted the marsupials, Australia did not become a part of this revolution and continued to produce new creatures of a marsupial order. We can say that except for the aquatic environment, every environment conquered here by placental animals was conquered by marsupial animals in Australia quite independently. All forms of life were explored, and all, or almost all, placental types were realized. There are marsupial wolves, marsupial foxes, bears, rodents, burrowing animals similar to moles, and marsupial monkeys. The wombat is similar to the woodchuck. The phalanger resembles the lemur. Like the civet cat, the dasyure has mottled fur, pointed ears, and a snake-like expression. Their teeth, their claws, and even their sizes are similar. Like the civet cat, the dasyure lives by night. Both are arboreal animals, feeding on other small animals, birds, and eggs. However, if we bear their origin in mind, both these animals, outwardly almost identical, are not even as close to each other as a whale is to a dog, or as we are to a bat: *they have evolved separately but parallelly in nature, just like the insectivores, carnivores, rodents, etc.,* where we find one offspring modeled on another. There are certainly no marsupial whales or dolphins. *There is certainly no marsupial man.* But when we look at a phalanger, we cannot help thinking with a little shudder that there is a completely similar placental counterpart to it situated somewhere near the stem of primates from which anthropoids and man himself have emerged. The phalanger is only a phalanger, but the process of humanization already shows us its first symptoms in this animal, as though humanization was the eventual fate of all biological evolution.

Naturally, the dasyure is not really modeled on the civet cat or the marten. The phalanger is not modeled on the lemur. The word "model" has no meaning in nature, which, as far as we know, does everything through the relation of cause and effect. The marsupial wolf would have been what it is even if the true wolf had not existed. Or, to explain it better, the reason that a marsupial wolf has been able to appear in Australia as a result of evolution is that the placental wolf was not there. The history of South American fauna also demonstrates this. For an enormous period, South America, like Australia, was an island where the peak of evolution was represented by marsupials and special placental orders. Then the Panama isthmus came out of the ocean, and other much more diversified placental mammals took advantage of this bridge (according to the rules) to invade a territory where life was possible and where they were not represented. There they competed with their counterparts, eliminating almost all of them. For every particular species of life, colonized separately by two creatures of different ancestry, only one can subsist; and only one subsisted. The fact that so many Australian animals appear familiar to us, although their origin is unrelated (at least not closely related) to the models they seem to have copied, is, in reality, one of the most revealing facts concerning the universal motivating powers of life that can be observed on our planet. But this fact has only slightly surprised naturalists. It teaches us that identical environments produce (according to Lamarck) or select (according to Darwin) similar living creatures. One single correlation could be accidental. But this is a constant in nature.

High altitude fauna and flora show common characteristics even when the mountains are far apart and have had no phylogenetic relationship for tens of millions of years. The fauna of the Sahara resembles that of the South African, Australian, South American, and

Asiatic deserts. The fauna of the South Pole resembles that of the North Pole. In the mud flats of the Arcachon basin, Lucien Cuenot found a whole range of aquatic animals similar to those listed by Davenport in other identical mud flats in the bay at Cold Spring Harbor, Long Island, New York. We could continue this list further. The meaning of all this is clear: the form of a living creature, its possibilities, and its adaptations are dictated by the environment where it developed, not by its biological origin. When the last ichthyosaurus died, the first dolphin was still lost in a future several tens of millions of years away, and the animal which after an enormous period of evolution was destined to become the dolphin was still running about on four legs on firm ground, as ignorant of both ichthyosaurus and dolphin as the cat that is watching me write these lines.

Should the first astronauts landing on a planet similar to earth expect to find creatures similar to those we know—and similar to ourselves? Knowing that the earth has never stopped evolving and that the creatures of bygone eras occasionally differ greatly from those of our time, it is hard, in effect, to see how nature could go back on her word to the extent of violating a law whose constancy she shows us here on earth every day. If other planets similar to the earth do exist elsewhere in the sky, they must have creatures similar to us. Or at least, their evolution must have developed more or less similarly to ours, with identical chronological cycles: as similar, for example, as the parallel evolution of marsupial and placental mammals, or the gastropoda, crustaceans, crabs, and sea anenomes of Arcachon and Cold Spring Harbor. A different origin must lead to anatomical differences, just as an identical environment produces identical appearance and behavior: for example, creatures with a human appearance (symmetry in relation to a vertical plane, two free upper limbs, a series of duplicate organs on either side of the plane assuring localization parallax, a central cybernetic system corresponding to our encephalon, etc.), but having neither the metabolism, reproductive system, skeleton, vegetative organs, nor perhaps the chemical composition of the human body.

It is highly likely that such creatures do exist in space in a great many parts of the sky. The trouble is that we do not know any of these places because the only planetary system that astronomy is presently studying is our own, and it comprises only one earth. Mars and Venus, the two planets closest to ours in distance and structure, are nevertheless so different from our earth that none of the arguments given above applies to them other than negatively: similar creatures require similar environments. We can only be sure that Martians or Venusians similar to man could no more exist than birds underwater or fish nesting in the trees. If Martians or Venusians do exist, which science is still far from being able to determine, they are certainly very different from us since they must be adapted to unique environments that have almost nothing in common with the earth.

But what would interest us the most is not primarily to know if there are creatures in space with two arms and two legs, hair like ours, two separate sexes, and blue or brown eyes. A gorilla resembles us more than a cat or a dog, yet we have more contact with cats and dogs. It would not matter if the Martians were green and had tentacles if they could reason like us, explore the universe with science identical to ours, and share the same ideas. It is the daily practice of these ideas that convinces us that we are thinking creatures.

Two prisoners locked away for life in two neighboring cells can never get together except by knocking on the intervening wall, and yet they are friends. They exchange their deepest thoughts, experience the same anguish and the same joy. If one of these hermits is a green Martian with tentacles and the other a man, they can still reach the highest pinnacles of thought together without ever knowing they are different. This at any rate is universal opinion. A great majority of men who have thought about this question are convinced that it is self-evident that if there are some forms of superior thought somewhere in this universe, intellectual contact with them would not pose a problem. Science fiction writers are in agreement here with philosophers and the man in the street. In order to strike an understanding with the green Martian, when we meet him, we will simply have to show him a mathematical proof. *As there could be only one form of mathematics,* the Martian will understand us straightaway.

In fact, nothing is so unsure. Reason has existed on this planet for only a few tens of thousands of years. It has been applied to scientific method for only a few centuries, and it has already extended to theories of relativity and the conquest of the atom nucleus. What are a few centuries in biological evolution? What levels of thought will have been reached in a billion years? We are as far from comprehending it as an amoeba is from Einstein. It is quite probable that no intellectual contact will be possible between man, even a brilliant man, and a form of thought far in advance of his, and so here our speculations reach a dead end.

If terrestrial evolution does teach us something about cosmic thought, it is only that the creature called man marks the starting point, the small and modest beginning of deliberative thought. We are at the source of this thought, and we have absolutely no idea what currents it is destined to flow into, nor what oceans it is destined to cross.

But, even if all thought superior to our own must, by definition, remain foreign to us, this is not necessarily the same for technologies. We do not know how a beehive thinks, what its thought process is, nor how thought is experienced by a bee. On the other hand, since Réaumur, we do know that the angles of a honeycomb cell correspond exactly to an engineer's calculations for obtaining the most economical and solid reservoir. The thinking of a beehive has nothing in common with human thought unless the object of thought is the same. Whatever the mental mechanisms of a swarm of bees may be, they result in a technology which is that of the human engineer. And what I have just said about the bee and about man is also valid for all other animal technologies.

We know nothing about the way animals have gone about developing the countless procedures they use other than that their method has nothing in common with ours. But out of these unrelated methods, some end in identical results: the wasp makes the same paper as we do, the ray torpedo fish can send electrostatic charges of the same type as ours, and like us the bee uses evaporation to produce coldness; the lion-ant and the engineer who constructs bridges and highways must use the same equilibrium gradients and so on. These facts are so true that for a few years now, a new science, bionics, has developed. Its aim is the systematic exploration of animal techniques. *For the first time, human science is applying itself to a nonhuman school of thought.*

The very existence of bionics and its success shows that in the

The Eurypterus lacustris, which once lived in the waters near Buffalo, New York—more than three hundred fifty million years ago—is a strange creature that has no equivalent in nature today.—Document André Bonne

technological domain the same needs create the same accomplishments. Wasp and printer have few similarities. But both need paper, and this paper is made. Here, too, observation of nature shows that we are dealing with a universal law, which, moreover, is only a specific case of the law of convergence analyzed above. Just as identical environments create similar creatures, likewise identical problems produce similar behaviors. The pike, the hippopotamus, and the nightingale have all separately discovered the meaning of owning property and react identically when confronted with a rival or trespasser.

But at the limit of behavior, we find psychism, and here I would like to suggest an argument that may be presumptuous but one that I believe justified by what I have written above. When a living species is confronted with a problem of survival, it must resolve the problem or disappear. If several species are confronted with an identical problem having only one solution, then the surviving species have all adopted this solution (for example, we have seen it in the "form of fish" and in defending one's territory). This is convergence.

But experimental science is completely based on one single principle. In its entirety, and by definition, it proceeds from one single process, *which is the reproducible experiment with a single solution.* If we know that there is iron in a given distant star, it is because a thousand experiments made on stimulated iron atoms have shown that they regularly give one spectrum, *and only one,* and, inversely, because this spectrum always reveals the presence of iron *and only iron.* The basic hypothesis of human science is that any experiment performed here can be repeated on Sirius, and that, given the same conditions, it will produce the same result. Moreover, this hypothesis has been proved adequately enough to be called a certainty.

So it seems that scientific knowledge *arising from experimentation* must be considered as the convergence ground for all the *psychisms* of the universe. The centuries that we have lived since the Renaissance have seen humanity gradually educated to this form of thought; and these centuries, in the evolution of our planet, correspond to the crucial period of passing from terrestrial thought to the preliminaries of cosmic thought. Man is in the process of discovering by himself the first words of a language that belongs to every galaxy. This lonely stammering resembles a child's stuttering, and, like that, it no doubt precedes and prepares for the bewilderment of our consciousness which is waking up to the world and to itself.

Thus a new humanity is gestating, and its prime characteristic will be universality. Everything is predicting this metamorphosis, which Professor Prat has already termed *"explosive"* because of the lightening acceleration of the historical changes just past. With their original peculiarities of language, race, and ideology at last overcome, men who, until now, were backing into the future (to use Valéry's apt expression) are now going to have the leisure and the power to turn around and walk *face forward toward the future.* For scientific language, which already permits all men to understand each other, is also the language of the sidereal civilizations preceding us in this change to universality. And these civilizations, of which we still know nothing but which will be revealed to us through space exploration, are what we shall be tomorrow. This may be the last lesson given us by the history of terrestrial life. If it does not allow us to foresee our distant future (for the simple reason that this future will be the creation of a way of thinking superior to ours, that of our descendants), it at least advises us that man is both an end and a beginning.

Born out of the earthly virtualities, man completes and caps animal evolution and, by the invention of science, opens the door to unfathomable cosmic evolution. He is a transitory creature between two levels. And doubtlessly all the living planets of the universe have created him, in one form or another, or will create him. The mollusks of the Arcachon basin, or the Cold Spring Harbor mollusks, grappling with the same problems, have come up with the same solutions. Two identical environments have produced similar creatures. *And the actual human environment is universal.* Our astronomers are studying the same universe as the astronomers of the Andromeda nebula. And so are our physicists and our chemists. Even if our bodies are different, which is most probable, our minds must have some common forms of development.

The beginnings of science are no doubt the same from one end of the sky to the other, even if the methods used to show the way are as different as the methods for making paper, as adopted by wasps in contrast to human industry.

We are living these beginnings of science now. What awaits us beyond is, by definition, inconceivable to our twentieth-century brains. Doubtlessly above the human level there begins a psychic abyss, which is as boundless as the abyss of time, called "the third infinity" by Teilhard de Chardin. An infinite time is a long time. But why be afraid of it? We have eternity in front of us.

Aimé Michel

Three Billion Years
of Life

Introduction

⸙

A Mystical Communion

⸙

It happened in Italy during the war. We had received a few days leave between two battles. I immediately set out for the rear with my faithful comrades at arms, Stitou and Guevarra: Stitou, a sturdy-legged Moroccan; and Guevarra, a hot-blooded driver.

The din of the bombs that had demolished Cassino still resounded in our ears, and their clouds of dark dust still rose up grimly before our eyes as we made our way into the quiet Italian countryside. And then, on entering a little wood, a new spectacle caught our attention. Under the peaceful foliage of the young trees, a young child was keeping watch over a dog and a lamb. The dog was romping around the child. The lamb was running after the dog. The child's peaceful gaze passed from one to the other.

And thoughtfully, we watched the harmony of these three creatures.

A little later, under the blue sky of Gargliano, among the spring flowers, we had just finished loading our guns when we spotted a stray bull. Fresh meat for men saturated with canned food—what a piece of good luck! We immediately organized a roundup. Soon the animal was cornered. There we were, Stitou, Guevarra, myself, and three others, surrounding it: makeshift butchers with guns in hand. Out of breath, and head down, the bull was staring at us in terror.

And nobody dared to shoot.

There are bonds linking us to life, to animals, and even plants, to everything that lives and dies like us.

I can still remember some words from an old woman that I heard when I was a child. She was said to be a theosophist. A theosophist? The word had seemed strange to us.

One day we were walking in the country with her. It was a beautiful day, and we were without a care. But then on a bank at the side of the path, we spotted some nettles. We ran to them straightaway and began crushing them with sticks. Then the old woman stopped us with one gesture.

"What have the nettles done to you?"

We were surprised. Naturally we thought, "Nettles sting." But, as a matter of fact, they had not stung us. We were quiet.

"Well," said the old woman, "leave them alone!"

Leave the nettles alone? Let them live in peace? For a moment we wanted to laugh, and the old woman seemed strange to us. We were children.

But since then, who would dare to say that she was completely wrong?

Who, in his lifetime, has not met his nettle?

Yes, we strongly feel that there is a bond linking us to the nettle and the bull, to the lamb and the dog, to all present-day living creatures, and even to fossils, to the creatures of today and those of yesterday.

But who can guarantee to us that this is not merely sentiment or, perhaps, an illusion?

At this point, the chemist and the biologist intervene, one armed with his distilling flask, the other with his microscope. And both of them address us in the same language, that of strictly measured words and cold reason.

First the chemist explains that there is a great resemblance between man and other living creatures. The chemical composition of man and that of some animals and plants has been analyzed. Exact measurements have been made of their compounds. And everywhere, the same types of atoms were found in more or less the same proportions, with only slight differences. For example, there is much less of a difference between man and alfalfa than between alfalfa and any mineral, stone, or metal. All living creatures—animals, men, or plants —are much closer to each other than to anything inanimate. The proportions of their elements bear witness to this. This can be seen displayed in the bottles exhibited in our museums. And this is all the more remarkable because these are not haphazard proportions. Carbon, for example, is thirty times more abundant in living creatures than in any other terrestrial matter, be it air, water, or rock. And what is more, these atoms, of which some are so strongly concentrated in air, water, and rock, are grouped in living creatures in larger and much more complex structures. In living creatures, they are grouped in sugar molecules, fat, carbide or protein molecules, which are extremely characteristic and which are found to be in almost identical proportions in man and in all plants and animals. Nothing in the present mineral world resembles these, even distantly, with the exception of petroleum, carbon, or amber, which do, in fact, originate from fossil matter that is extinct today. And, among the molecules thus compared, the most important in the creature's life, those controlling its way of feeding and growing, are the same in plant or animal species which are often very different. For example, hormones extracted from roosters or frogs also act on man, and vice versa.

Here the biologist can supply us with more information. The antitoxins produced in the bodies of horses can act on man, when they are injected. This sort of experimentation has passed the laboratory stage. It is now a part of practical medicine. It is the basis of serum treatment. Our whole struggle against tetanus and diphtheria is based on it. If worried mothers no longer have to watch over near-suffocating children as they had to a century ago, we owe this to the identical nature of the antitoxins from man and horses.

But let us pass to a new level of organization, the one revealed by the microscope. Once again, we find identity in the elementary form of all creatures, that is, in the cell. With a few variations, we find that the cell is the same from man to animals to the most simple plants and even down to bacteria. And the structure of the cell is highly characterized and organized, consisting of an envelope, a principal mass, and a nucleus, with each part having its own special characteristics and properties.

On a different level again, we have the size of the organ or the individual. Once again there is unity. Man is made on the same plan as roosters or frogs: a careful glance at their skeletons is sufficient to prove this. Of course, there are differences, but on the other hand, what a lot of similarities! Vertebrae, shoulder blades, ribs, bones of the limbs, or the skull: corresponding parts are easily recognized. The dog that offers us a paw to shake shows us its wrist half bent. Its elbow is back and quite high, almost on a level with its chest. In the frog's front leg, the elbow is more detached and even better recognizable.

When several people get together, we try to guess their relationship and their common origin. Man, animals, and plants, from the atomic level to the individual level, passing through the molecules and the cells, show resemblances noted by common sense and confirmed by modern science. These resemblances are countless and striking. Do they imply a common origin? It is right to wonder. Is the relationship a close or a distant one? Is it purely natural or is it, in the last analysis, the fact of a common force superior to nature?

To hope to answer these questions, or at least ask them more accurately, we must review the history of life on earth. And this is what we are going to do in the pages that follow.

Knowledge of this history is dependent on its own methods, of which we shall get an idea first. Thus armed, we can look at the possible origin of life on earth, the great crisis that it has passed through, and the laws, less spectacular perhaps but in reality more important, that life has obeyed. Through the creatures—and occasionally they are strange creatures—that we shall describe, there arises the problem of biological evolution, the origin of the species. We shall portray it in its historical aspect and, better still, in its essential aspect: that of a temporal development through which life has gradually made its way toward the blossoming of humanity.

PART I

THE DEVELOPMENT OF LIVING MATTER

CHAPTER I

✔

Fossils and Dates

✔

The word *fossil* comes from a Latin word meaning "to dig." A fossil, in the broad, original sense of the word, is something that can be found or discovered by burrowing and digging in earth or rock; in particular, it is the remains or traces of a prehistoric animal or plant. But fossils, no matter how carefully we study them, do not give us information of the same kind nor the same standard as present-day living creatures. Between the evidence of past life and that of present life, there is an enormous frequency difference. Among present-day living creatures, we can study any given individual we choose, merely by wanting to, or by paying the required price. The rarest fish can be obtained; the recent example of the coelacanth from the Comoro Islands has shown us that. On the other hand, preserved fossils make up only a minute part of the ancient creatures. And of these ancient creatures, we do not study those that we wish to, but those that we can, the ones discovered by us. In a way, it is a difference similar to the difference between voting by universal suffrage, and an inquiry made by Gallup poll, where only a few voters are questioned.

As a rule, in the Gallup polls, the witnesses are not chosen, but are picked at random. And if they are not—for example, if the large manufacturers are questioned or if the workmen are questioned—then the results risk being slanted in one direction or another, and therefore they do not give an accurate idea of the real opinion of the social body. The same risk exists for fossils, our witnesses of past life. In order to be sure the witnesses are part of a past reality, that

33

our fossils belong to a previous living world, we must be able to take into account the more or less great probabilities that a creature, or part-creature, was confronted with to become fossilized. And for that, unfortunately, we do not yet have any numerical statistics, or at least very few. Instead, we have good qualitative knowledge. Consider the living world with its plants and animals at a given period in the past. A host of creatures, perhaps the majority of them, are eaten by others, either while they are still alive or after their death. Of these creatures, nothing remains, except the rarest contents of their consumers' stomachs, miraculously preserved. On the other hand, if the creature under consideration escaped being eaten, its eventual fate nevertheless is death. If this is a terrestrial creature, it is most likely its corpse will decompose. Then the hard parts, bones or shells, are dissolved by the rain, broken, gnawed, or dispersed in a state of unrecognizable fragments. This, among other reasons, explains the very great scarcity of bird fossils. We only have three specimens of the rarest and most ancient bird fossil, the *Archaeopteryx*. In the water and slime, the soft parts of soft creatures almost never leave any trace. We can count on our fingers the fossil remains of jellyfish or tubeless worms. And the hard parts are not always preserved; they can be dissolved or gnawed. This probably explains the relative rarity of fish fossil skeletons. All in all, it is much more probable for a living creature not to be fossilized. There are exceptions, for example the foraminifera, tiny animals that abound in the sea, and whose shells accumulate on the ocean floor. But such cases are rare.

Among the tiny minority of creatures of which some traces have been preserved for us, several cases can be given.

Very rarely, the creature is completely fossilized. Thus, in common silica, examined in little splinters by microscope, we were surprised to discover unicellular animal forms, so well preserved that one daring naturalist tried treating them with coloring agents to color the organic matter of the actual cells; and he was successful. The cell fossils are colored in all their detail: cytoplasm, nucleus, and the tiny flagella. Thus the organic matter is preserved almost intact, as it was one hundred or one hundred and fifty million years ago. For this to have happened, the cell must have been seized very quickly and protected. We guess that it was protected by the silica gel, which then, and perhaps very soon, became consolidated into chalcedony.

Imprint of a sea-reptile skeleton—Photo Henry Corson

In any case, its ability to take coloring agents like living cells clearly shows the constancy of the chemical characteristics of living matter throughout time.

In Poland, the same protective chalcedony has preserved admirable structures of creatures by enclosing them in little compartments. These structures, which puzzled us for a long time, were called graptolites. Thanks to this chalcedony, we know that these were attached to the base of the same ancestral trunk as vertebrates; in short, they are rather tenuous great-great-uncles of ours.

In other cases, it can be resin, secreted by the conifers, which has engulfed flowers, insects, centipedes, and spiders, and which has become the amber found in the area of East Prussia, Poland, and

Lithuania, and is used in jewelry for women. In Galicia (Spain), a sort of wax associated with petroleum embalmed the corpses of mammoths and woolly rhinoceroses more than ten thousand years ago and mummified them.

In Siberia, mammoths have been buried in the ice or in the frozen ground since the last ice age, and they are preserved to this day as they were, with their flesh and their hair. They have been exploited for the ivory of their gigantic tusks and even for their meat, the oldest frozen meat, since it dates from at least ten thousand years B.C. The natives used to dig it up with a pick and shovel; the rare Europeans who had the privilege of getting snacks at this strange butcher shop, Father Breuil and others, found it a bit leathery, if truth be told.

The Siberian mammoths are among the oldest known fossils. According to Pliny, in the fourth century B.C., Theophrastus already knew that ivory was being extracted from the earth. In the ninth century A.D., the Arabs were buying fossil ivory coming from a market on the Volga river. The first Chinese emperor of the Manchu dynasty, Kang-Hi, who reigned from 1662 to 1725, wrote in his work about the animal world: "The ancient Chin-i-King speaks of the hidden mouse and the mother of the mice, and the 'Mirror of the Manchu Language' speaks of the ice rat. In the North, in the country of the Russians, near the sea, there is a species of rats as big as elephants, which live in the ground, and which die as soon as they come up to the air, or when the sunlight hits them."

The old Manchu emperor added, "There are hidden rats weighing up to five tons. The natives of the North get their bowls, combs, knife handles, etc., from their teeth. I, myself, have seen these teeth and these instruments, and I believe there is truth in these old books." In 1771, a new edition of the "Mirror of the Manchu Language" states that "we can eat the flesh of the ice rat or the rat from the mountain streams," that its hair is several feet long, and that carpets can be woven from it.

The inhabitants of Kamchatka, U.S.S.R., talk about Touila, a person who moves about under the ice in a sleigh drawn by a dog called Kozei. When they have arrived at their destination, Kozei shakes the snow from his hair, and this is what causes earthquakes. The Alaskan Eskimos tell the story of a whale called Kilu.

"Kilu used to live in the sea: she had an argument with Algu, another sea monster, who chased her from the sea. On land, Kilu wanted to move about, but she was so heavy that she sank into the ground and began to swim. She had long tusks like walruses. Not so long ago, the Kilus used to surface quite often and their tusks could be seen pointing above the ground, so they could easily be attacked. But today the Kilus have become suspicious. They no longer come up so often in their lifetime. Those that are found are corpses, which come up close to the surface of the ground, like whale corpses stranded on the shore."

Ingenious myths, but they contain a host of accurate observations; for example, it is obvious that the people of the North did first exploit the mammoths which gave away their whereabouts by their tusks sticking out of the ground, and then later, the others. By their obvious and gross factual errors, primitive myths can shock us, but we can see in them an attempt to associate several problems in order to explain them. In this, they show a praiseworthy effort of the human mind aspiring for unity.

The same indulgence is needed for cases much closer to us: At Valencia in Spain, a mammoth's tooth was held in reverence for a long time as a relic of Saint Christopher. In 1789, Furon relates that "the monks of Saint Vincent used to carry one of the Saint's bones in procession with them, and this was found to be a mammoth's femur."

However, it was almost a century ago that the mammoth became known in Europe. Discovered by the Cossacks, it is mentioned as an elephant in a Russian grammar book published at Oxford in 1696. In 1704, in a work published at Amsterdam, it was described as a fossil, and since then has been considered as a fossil, and rightly so. In addition to the mammoth, we also find the woolly rhinoceros in the ice of the Siberian soil. This creature is also extinct. But such cases of flesh and bone preservation, as surprising as they are, both in themselves and by their history, are nevertheless rare exceptions.

The pollens and spores, tiny grains, a fine powder, that the wind carries away and scatters, are much more frequently preserved. Occasionally too, animal epidermis can be mummified by nature; plants become carbonized. In coal, the parts that stain the fingers are made up of tiny pieces of wood that have become like charcoal. Other times, it is the hard parts, such as minerals, bones, teeth, or shells which are buried and preserved. Most of them are calcareous. Bones and teeth are also rich in phosphates. Some shells contain a lot of silica, such as diatoms and radiolaria, tiny creatures that float in the water. The little spicules that we find tangled together in the flesh of sponges consist of calcium salts in some species and of silica in others.

But there are inconsistencies. For example, in Cambodia and in the Glass Mountains in the United States, dating from a little more than two hundred million years ago, the shells are made of flint, whereas generally the same species are calcareous. And sponge spicule fossils normally made of silica are by exception found to be made of calcium. Since nothing like this has ever been observed in living creatures, the most simple explanation is that after death, the original mineral has dissolved and been replaced by another. This seems all the more probable since we know of examples in the inert world where crystals of one mineral can finally be transformed into another mineral. The matter is that of the second mineral while the crystalline form remains that of the first.

In addition, living creatures, their remains and theid dead bodies, have a marked tendency (occasionally easily explained) to attract foreign substances or in some way to concentrate them, not only where the minerals of their own hard parts are localized, but within or around them too. This is so for glauconite, a sea mineral that molds the interior of foraminiferan shells or sponge spicules. Often the ammonite casts are made of iron pyrites, which gives them an unusually bright aspect, the color of brass. Occasionally it is concentrated around the fossil or its imprint. The siliceous sands around Mainz in Germany conceal nodules as large as a fist, made of baryta. If we break them, we sometimes discover the imprint of shellfish or of a cone from a resinous tree. Such nodules are greatly sought after by collectors.

In layers near the surface of the ground in western France, oyster fossils or other shellfish can be found. Their surface has pretty patterns on it, with recurring motifs made up of more or less concentric zones that remind one of small round loaves of bread or the braid trimmings our grandmothers used to delight in wearing in their young days. Each shell has ten or twenty of these joined motifs. If we put a drop of acid on them, surprisingly enough, there is no effect, no boiling. Thus, unlike all other self-respecting oysters, these shells are no longer calcareous. After all the tests have been completed, we see that they are made of a type of chalcedony. Here again, there has been a substitution, but its beauty should not mask its evil-doing from us: in effect, the original details of the surface are masked or effaced here. This usually happens when dolomite has replaced the calcium. So we must be careful when we try to understand fossils that are unluckily transformed like this. Other times though, the transformations can be favorable. It can happen that trunks or pieces of wood, instead of rotting, become completely impregnated with silica, thus becoming as hard and as beautiful as agate. The Sahara and Arizona deserts offer splendid examples dating back tens of millions of years. In general, the structure of the wood tissues stays preserved in its pattern as pure and as distinct as microscopic cross sections of present-day wood.

It also can happen that the living creature completely disappears, hard parts as well as soft ones, but not without first leaving its imprint in the sediment that is still soft. This is how the elegant leaf and fern patterns have arisen in the schists interposed between layers of coal. Sometimes it is a cast from the exterior, and sometimes from the interior.

These casts are valuable evidence. A host of details can be read from them: where the soft parts are placed; how the very sinuous partitions dividing the shell of the ammonites into compartments are laid out. In the phosphates at Quercy, internal casts of the cranium of small mammals show us the delicate form of their cerebrum.

Usually, the casts and imprints are set in a fine mud, which was soft at first and then became solidified. At Solenhofen, in Bavaria, Germany, limestone has provided animal imprints of rare beauty. The grain of it is invisible to the eye and for a long time the rock has provided excellent stones for engraving. These fossil imprints are rare, but they are so accurate, that, for example, we can identify the successive traces of the same crab carcass, as it was pushed along by the wind in spurts, and eventually came to rest at the edge of the lagoon. In the Massif Central in France, leaf imprints and imprints of other parts of plants have been preserved by volcanic ashes or by the calcareous deposits of certain petrifying springs and waters. Else-

These imprints are set in earth that was soft at first and then hardened—Photo from *Aus Jahrenmillionen*

Brachiopod of the Jurassic period. —Photo François Garnier

where, the internal cast of the fossils is made of glauconite, pyrites, or other minerals. We have come to wonder whether the organic matter of the corpse has not directly or indirectly favored a concentration of these minerals.

Thus when they examine rocks, geologists try to find a meaning in the slightest detail or sign. Parallel lines, pairs of holes sideways, or like a scratch mark, reveal the tracks of worms or crabs. We have found fossilized eggs, fetuses in their mothers' wombs, even excrement, which we can trace back to the animals they came from.

Once the fossils have been gathered on the ground, the geologist's job is by no means over. We could even say that it is just beginning. Not only must these fossils be examined to see what they have to offer us, but we must also try to discover what they do not show us.

The first job is to detach them from the rock or gangue that they are attached to. Then we proceed to a laboratory, where we see the specialists at work. Here, with a hammer, a man steadily breaks up schists: one blow and the block splits open and a fish imprint appears, its scales still shining. No, it wasn't a miracle. The block broke in accordance with a surface of least resistance, and generally the extremities of fossils are such surfaces. But, a stroke with the hammer must be given at the right spot, in the right direction, and with the desired strength. This takes competency, intuition, and perspicacity. This man used to be a truck driver, but his ability to break stones was discovered, and he was promoted to technician. Further on, an aging assistant, with his hammer and drill in his hand, removes the last splinters: a test of his skill and patience. In the next room there is a light buzzing. In the hands of an expert, the drill and hammer are replaced by a large metallic pencil which vibrates by itself, a sort of miniature vibrator.

We go on to another laboratory. Under a hood in front of a faucet, with a big pan in his hands, shirt sleeves rolled up, who is the boy in a blue apron? A laboratory assistant? No! He is a leading specialist in foraminifera. He puts down his pan and explains his method to us. Taking one or two kilograms of chalk, he mixes it with water by hand. He lets it stand, then decants the water, and begins again as many times as are necessary. The chalk disappears, and the precious little shells remain mixed with other fossil debris and grains of sand. He sieves and dries it, and then he can start examining it with the microscope.

We admired the simplicity of the method and the cheapness of the material. However the pan has one drawback. It does not represent progress; it is not expensive enough. The laboratory will not receive great esteem from high places. But, show people expensive and complicated equipment, even if it is of no help, and you will be Somebody in their eyes. The great esteem goes to the wealthy laboratories. The poor get nothing. Send for the latest model micro-vibra-tool from Sweden or America, and the prestige of your investment will reflect back on you.

All the same, I have met two men who insisted that they preferred simple methods and inexpensive equipment. One man was the elderly Mr. Wuitner, founder of the Levallois-Perret Naturalists' Association in France. The other man was Professor Goldsmith from the University of Oslo, one of this century's greatest petrographers.

But let us continue our round of the laboratories, rich or poor (because the poor ones dream of becoming rich), and there we shall see many diversified apparatus and methods at work. Over here, a whole arsenal of needles are used to extricate the fossils. Over there, a dentist's drill; elsewhere, a compressed carbonic gas spray, or a sand spray. To break stubbon blocks more easily, they can be heated until they are red hot: if they are cooled quickly enough, they may crack open. If the flame from a blow lamp is projected onto sandstone, the grains often break up.

If the gangue is calcareous, and if the fossil is siliceous, they are both treated with hydrochloric acid. Acetic acid (the acid in vinegar) is used for dolomite. To work on silica, it is necessary to use hydrofluoric acid, a reagent which is not as easy to handle since it must be kept in ebonite or plastic bottles because it attacks glass. A whole collection of other products are also used, all in the clever hands of experts. Solid caustic potash attacks clay; when dissolved, it helps to wash the chalk off foraminifera. Potassium chloride water bleaches the outside surface of plants; and collodion, by adhering to them, detaches them from their rocks. Methylene blue brings out foraminifera and calcareous algae.

To reveal the many details hidden within the shells, it is often worthwhile making a cast: for this plaster, wax, gelatin, or gutta is used. In the case of foraminifera, it is best to inject them with a resin, Canada balsam. Once this has hardened, the shell is dissolved in hydrochloric acid, and the balsam cast appears. The specialist can now study this to his heart's delight.

African geologists have observed that wear from natural friction with the sand has often brought out very fine details in fossils collected in the Sahara. From this observation came the idea of imitating the wind's action artificially. The sand spray or carbonic gas spray attends to this, and so the details of the interior, the partitions, and the most delicate sinuosities are brought out. Polishing has been in practice for a long time. Everyone has admired the sections of mollusk shells on certain marbles. In central Sweden, one can see cross sections of orthoceras in the sidewalks.

The polished cross sections are indispensable in reconstructing the structure and form of orthoceras, polyps, and wood fossils. Cross sections in series allow us to get an insight into the internal anatomy of animals as massive as the armor plated fish. We can even study the secrets of their nervous system.

Several decades ago, metallurgists invented metallography: in order to reveal the delicate structure of a metal and the architecture of the crystal bonds forming it, a plane surface is carefully polished, put under a strong light, and looked at by reflection through a microscope. The mosaic of the crystals can be seen in all its beauty. Naturally there have been bright geologists who have discovered that there are some rocks, like coal, so black and so opaque that no cross section can make them transparent. But they respond to the same examination by reflection. The difficulty for geologists has been finding a way to polish the carbon, which is much more delicate than metal. A little imagination and a lot of patience and testing have succeeded. And in the mass of a common piece of coal, impenetrable and formless up until then, we can see perfectly recognizable remains of wood becoming visible in the dull parts and very pretty spores and epidermis remains in the shinier parts, both preserved thanks to their chemical composition and their cutin which does not ferment. All around the uniform smooth mass that they are embedded in, is an ancient gel of carbonized organic matter.

Thus all methods, simple and complicated, ancient and modern are applied.

X-rays penetrating bodies that are opaque to light have had a surprising success. We have been able to see the twisted intestine of a sea urchin fossil through the shell, and the offspring of crinoids clasped in the flexuous arms of their mothers across schists that were too difficult to split.

In the drafting room, we have proportional compasses and a camera lucida. Often, too, we draw on photographs. The ordinary photo is not always adequate. By modifying it, we can perfect it. Occasionally the negative gives more expressive images; for example, the interior wall of the cranial bones, where it is like seeing a relief cast of the cerebrum. Instead of ordinary light, infrared has successfully been used for plant fossils and ultraviolet for fish scales and for wing fibers of air reptiles.

It can happen that a fossil shows patches of color, which a photo would reproduce or accentuate; these are often mere accidents with no interest at all for us. So, we mask them by dipping the specimen in a sublimate of ammonium chloride, which leaves a thin film of fine white powder on the surface. Then only the real relief details stand out. Of course, in all cases, the amount of light and shade is controlled by floodlights correctly positioned, with their beams crossed.

In the air, the fossil detail stands out well; if we plunge it into an appropriate bath, the relief is blurred, but other details appear. Turpentine in particular, spread in a film over the surface, allows us to see some shallow internal details in the shells of foraminifera and ammonites. This is no miraculous power, but simply an effect of the refractive index. The mineral of shells, whether it is calcite or aragonite, has a high refractive index. Air has a lesser index. A luminous ray between the two is usually reflected, hardly penetrating the interior of the mineral. If, instead of using air, we put a liquid with an index almost equal to that of the mineral in contact with the minerals, then the luminous rays penetrate further into the mineral, showing us the details of its arrangement.

We are amazed when confronted with the variety of methods that man has developed in the face of nature to decipher the history of life. It is only equaled by the variety of methods that nature has used to preserve the evidence of this history, such as, for example, the various fossilization procedures.

Man responds with an appropriate reaction to nature's action.

To unravel history, not only must we know the actors and the events, but we must also be able to ascribe dates. Since Stenon in the seventeenth century, we have had a simple method for doing this: the superposition of layers of earth.

Let's go to Cormeilles, in the country not far from Paris, among the rolling hills covered with fields, woods, and at one time even vines. In front of us, there is the Lambert quarry, two centuries old and one of the largest in Europe. Beneath us, over an area almost one-half mile wide and 200 feet deep, opened up by mechanical shovels, there appears tier after tier of parallel layers of earth, emphasizing the successive levels of exploitation. Layers of soft chalk containing some briny animal shells alternate with layers of gypsum, former lagoon deposits. Higher up there is limestone with fresh water mollusks, and higher still, a thin layer of gray chalk containing oyster casts, evidence of the sea's return. Then a thick layer of sand. Finally, on top, in the silica of the hard millstone grit, there are limnei casts, evidence of pools of fresh water. The layers follow each other from bottom to top. Each layer could only be deposited after the layer beneath it and before the layer on top of it. A mixture would be impossible for solid matter and over areas of this size.

We often find the same succession of layers from one locality to another. For example, gypsum that is so typical here is also found twenty to twenty-five miles farther to the east on the slopes of the right bank of the Marne river. Some kinds of chalk which the Cormeille drills have struck deep down are also found in the limestone at Fiz, in Savoie. From the Alps to the Himalayan ranges, ammonites recur. Since the end of the eighteenth century and Giraud-Soulavie and William Smith, we know that certain fossil species are found only in certain ground dating from a certain era: Lamarck's potamian for example, dating from fifty million years ago. A doubly interesting fact: it shows us regular variations in the succession of fauna, changes in the history of life; and it provides us with means of dating.

Fossils have helped us to discern, among other things, the misfortunes that the layers have undergone while being deposited or after they were deposited. In some places, certain stages are not represented. There are no chalk fossils in Alsace or around Alsace, either because no sediment was deposited or else because it was deposited and has since been removed by erosion.

In very broken up areas, where the regular succession of layers has been destroyed and their connections changed by internal forces which have broken and dispersed them, the fossils are a great help in discerning abnormal connections. In many parts of the French Alps and the Himalayan ranges, it has happened that a layer became broken up, then settled, and was then torn up again. Under this continuing pressure, older soil has been scattered by the movements of the fresher soil on top of it. Fossils bear witness to this and help us to avoid making serious mistakes.

While geologists were establishing relative chronology and gradually extending it over the entire surface of the earth, others were trying to attach geology to a known standard, to give it absolute values in years. When we have historical reference points like coins or sunken ships, the deposits of mud along the shores, the filling up of the lakes and river deposits permit us to evaluate the recent speed at which sediments are deposited and their thickness in one year. Allowing for speeds of the same rate in the past, and knowing the average thickness of former sediments from the various geological periods, we can make an evaluation and measure the approximate time they needed to be deposited.

This was the situation when the Swedish geologist Gerard de Geer thought up the first strict method for dating. He himself, a handsome old man, with a white beard and a perceptive, sharp look, told me about the circumstances that led to this method. He was studying quite recent terrane from the Quaternary period. Among the rocks near Stockholm, there was some gray clay deposited in the lakes as these glaciers had gradually receded. This clay, when seen closely, is composed of a superposition of thin layers which the Swedes call *varves*. Each varve has a clear and a dark layer, so they are easy to recognize, as they look like ribbons. The successive varves are not of the same thickness. One day, at one part of the clay pit, de Geer surveyed the successive thicknesses varve by varve and made a graph of them. Then because he was busy at the time with other research work, he put the graph away in a drawer and concentrated his efforts on other aspects of his work.

Twenty years later, de Geer decided to return to his interrupted work. In another clay pit at a nearby lake, he made another survey. Then he went back to his laboratory and compared it to the first one: they coincided. For example, in both of them, three thin varves were followed by a very thick one, then two thin ones, then four thick ones, and so on. If they are so regular, then the varves are not accidental. Each represents a melted deposit, probably from the same year. And from one lake to another, in the same year, the summer heat did not vary too much. The next day, de Geer sent his students out in pairs to make profiles, and he himself devoted forty years, the rest of his life, to this study. The first geochronological method was established.

It works on a simple principle. From one ancient lake to another, along the old head of the glacier, he surveyed the outlines to make sure they coincided. Then he followed the path by which the glacier had receded, and new lakes appeared. As one lake was filled, another would appear further to the north because of the receding glacier and the irregularities of its bed. The varves are evidence of this. And thus, a chronology was established, covering a span of more than ten thousand years, which eventually could be connected with the Christian era, thanks to objects from historical epochs.

At the beginning of this century, other methods were developing to date the strata where the history of life was inscribed. Radioactivity had just been discovered. Certain atoms split spontaneously: while giving off radiation, they lose some electrons and are thus transformed into another atom. A strange and important fact: the electrons that were eliminated occasionally will form a light atom like helium. All atoms of one kind will not split at the same time, far from it. If we study a group of atoms at a given time, half of them will still be intact at the end of a given period: and of this half there will still be half again the same amount of time again. That is a quarter of the original group; and so on indefinitely. If the same thing happened to the effective forces of the armies, the world soon would not have to fear war any more.

But let us return to radioactive atoms. Their application in dating rocks works on a simple principle. In the mineral being studied, we measure the proportions of the original atom and the one that stemmed from it. Knowing the time that it takes to divide into two, we can thus deduce how long ago the mineral was formed. Naturally we assume that the period itself has not varied during geological eras. We have proof of this in the aureoles surrounding certain minerals contained in the micas of the most ancient rocks, dating back several billions of years. The dimensions of these aureoles conform to the requirements of the law of present-day radioactivity. There are other difficulties and complications, but these themselves eventually provide the means for being solved.

When we began using these new dating methods around 1930, there was a lot of speculation as to whether the results would concur with the results from other methods or not and which one of the two forms of thought—that of the old geologists or that of the young physicists—would have to be reviewed and corrected.

Verifications were possible. One of the radioactive atoms is carbon 14, an isotope originally coming from the upper atmosphere, where it is continually being made by cosmic rays from nitrogen, and from there passing into the carbonic gas of the air, then into plant and animal tissue. It is measured mainly in bones and wood fossils. It dates back to around 30,000 or 40,000 B.C.

Some specimens from Germany and the United States have undergone double dating processes: by carbon 14 and by varves. And the results coincide at around 10,000 B.C., give or take about one hundred to two hundred years, which is within the limit of test errors.

A much longer period scale can be obtained from other atoms: lead isotopes, helium, strontium, potassium. They have been measured in a certain number of minerals from lodes, volcanic rocks, and other locations of heavy matter. These can also be dated in relation to the relative succession of sedimentary layers.

Thus we have the first method of evaluating the age of the earth itself. By grouping in twos the different isotopes of lead in ores of varying ages, we can determine the probable date of origin of terrestrial lead. The method was worked out by a Scotsman, Holmes; and a French geologist, Goguel, had the idea of representing the equations from it by threads stretched between two fragments of wood: a sort of harp whose cords would be crossed and oblique. If everything was accurate and exact, the threads should all pass through the same point. In reality, they only come close to the same point, as was seen in Goguel's harp. The zone where they come the closest together, and which marks the date of origin of terrestrial lead, is around three billion three hundred million to three billion five hundred million years ago.

But in addition, independently of these results, Holmes and other scientists collected samples of ore that were believed to be as old as was possible and tried to date them with other atoms or lead. The dates obtained varied greatly. Was the oldest date going to fit in with the three or four billion years? For a long time it was around two billion. Then the antiquity record rose. At the present time, the record belongs to a mica three billion four hundred million years old, and the maximum estimate is thus respected.

Likewise, using the effects of radioactivity, we have dated countless meteorites, which fall down to the earth from the cosmos. Until now, not one of them has been found to be older than four billion years; so this leads us to believe that they are a part of the solar system, like our globe, and that the globe is approximately this old.

Meanwhile the astronomers have not been idle. They have good grounds for believing that the stars which make up the universe, and whose apparent and majestic immobility can be seen on a clear night, are in reality in the process of separating from each other; the universe is expanding. Knowing the speed of this, we can then estimate at what period in the past all the stars were assembled together at the same point in a kind of gigantic atom, the "original atom" that Father Lemaître speaks of, an enormous mass out of which all stars, all of nature emerged, and in so doing became differentiated. The first date ascribed to this original atom was two billion years, but this was quite a lot less than the three or four billion years that physicists had assigned to earth, and the earth is believed to have derived from this original atom. There was a gross contradiction. Luckily, in the meanwhile, a new and more powerful telescope was installed at Mount Palomar. Thanks to this, mistakes were found in the previous estimations, and the probable origin of the visible expansion of the universe was pushed back to about twelve or fourteen billion years. So there remains a large margin of time between the formation of solar system and that of the earth.

However, for the past twenty years, astronomers studying time have been put to a hard test. An hour is one twenty-fourth of a day; a day is the time that the earth takes to rotate once. These definitions appear simple to us. But in reality they are not. The time of one revolution varies by a few minutes according to the season. So, we have adopted its average time during the year as our standard. But very accurate measurements, gathered in observatories for a hundred years and studied for the past twenty years, have shown that it is not a fixed standard. The day is getting slightly slower. Why? Probably because of braking due to the friction of the tides, which in turn is due mainly to the attraction of the moon. If this hypothesis is true, then we can work out a braking equation. Then we can work back to a date where the equation is no longer possible, which is the date of the formation of the Earth-Moon couple. This date is about three billion four hundred million years ago, coinciding with the date obtained by previous methods.

Finally, four other methods give the same results. But as they are based on the history of life on earth, we shall deal with them as they arise further on in this book. All in all, we can admit for the time being that our earth was consolidated about four billion years ago. But recent experience forces us to be careful and to foresee that corrections may have to be made in the future as they have been made in the recent past.

✓

CHAPTER II

Proof of Evolution

✓

It is a lovely Parisian spring day, so let us go to the sand pit at Auvers, which is near the very pretty village with old houses and lots of trees of the kind the Impressionist painters used to like. In the layers of sand, we can gather all sorts of different shells by the handful: narrow ones and wide ones, big ones and little ones, all types of shells, periwinkles, clams. It is just like being by the seaside, because one could say that these shells are just like those on our beaches. But they are not. If we have the patience to collect some, wrap them carefully so that they won't break, put them into bags, label them, carry them back, and compare them to present-day shell collections in a museum or laboratory, then we will be able to see differences between every shell from Auvers and its cousin on our beaches today. In this one, a tooth protrudes more; in that one, the grooves are not as pronounced; in others there are three rows of spikes instead of four. The ancient and present species are different when examined in detail. Yet they have astonishing similarities as far as their main features are concerned. When two men look alike, we are tempted to think, "they are related."

Isn't it the same for species?

And so, the fossils pose one of the major problems of the history of life through the ages: the origin of the species.

Two solutions are possible. One is the immutability of species; species are stable and unrelated. The other solution is the doctrine of evolution: species are derived one from the other; in the end all are derived from one single, very simple, original species, or perhaps a

51

A tuna, which used to swim in the Tyrrhenian sea fifty million years ago.—Document André Bonne

very small number, which then became diversified during the ages. Life is similar to the trunk of a tree, which has divided into many branches.

Two extreme theories. One sees every species as being independent. The other sees them all linked to each other. But the gardener or farmer have something to say here—good, simple, common sense. The gardener will tell us that a plum stone has always given a plum tree, and a cherry stone a cherry tree. So, at first glance immutability seems true. At best, evolution is only a rare minute case, an exception to the great law of heredity. Immutability is the rule; animals and plants are born out of, and according to, their own species.

Would there be room for an intermediary, more cautious opinion somewhere between these two? Some people have thought so. They have admitted that species of the same kind, a horse and donkey for example, could have come from the same model, from the same common trunk. On the other hand, species that had more differences would be independent of each other. But in the eighteenth century, Buffon saw the weakness of this view: if we agree that nature could make a creature of a different species from one given creature, then we cannot deny that she could make the same possibility work for a creature of another genus, because the limits of genera are only conventional. Often there are species that we hesitate to classify in one genus or another—plum trees and wild cherry trees, for example. If plum trees are derived one from the other, and likewise cherry trees, then plum trees and cherry trees should stem from a common trunk. Once we have started down the path of evolution, it is impossible to stop half way. It is all or nothing.

The great law of experience, propounded by our forefathers— hunters, shepherds, or farmers—is consecrated in the Bible, where we read in the Book of Genesis that God created the animals and plants "each according to his own kind." How could it have said anything else to the ancient Hebrews? Could it have made those wise shepherds believe that ewes could once have given birth to kids, or goats given birth to lambs? But by stating "each according to his own kind," it implied that God Almighty was the creator and initiator not only of things but of the order of things. And in order to imply this, the Bible used language that the shepherds could understand most easily.

Thirty centuries later, when we compare the development of the individual and the development of the species, and when Haeckel irreligiously but voluminously wrote that "the act of reproduction is only an excess of growth of the organism," are we so far from the double law that God gave to his creatures in Genesis: "Be fruitful and multiply"?

Not far from the Hebrew people, several centuries B.C., an Arab sect, the Gerbanites, were admitting the germ of new ideas: every 36,425 years, no more and no less, new and different species replaced the old ones. Perhaps the observation of fauna fossils was the origin of this strange myth. But in any case, there was not the slightest trace yet of the idea of evolution or relationships.

The Greeks show some glimpses of it. But only glimpses. When Anaximander said that the first men were derived from fish, this was only a specific case, not a general theory, and the problem was less one of the development of the human species than the problem of its first representatives. With no mother to carry them, where could the first embryos have developed? With Empedocles and his theory of separate organs combining by chance, we have a general theory of the origin of life, but it does not account for the derivation of species. It was his view that among the countless combinations formed, a large number were unstable and had been eliminated. It is true that this idea is a distant announcement of Darwin's later theory of natural selection. And finally, Aristotle claimed incidentally that living creatures could be formed from inert matter.

Here, as in other fields of scientific thought, the Romans contributed nothing.

Among the first Christian doctors, several, like Grégoire de Nysse, have broad views. Nemesius, the Bishop of Emesus speaks of the "type of relationship" that unites all living creatures. Saint Augustine wrote: "The production of living creatures was complete from the beginning only in their principle and in their cause because God did not create all nature at the first attempt." But then, during the whole Middle Ages and even later, the words of the Bible were interpreted literally. Since the origin of the species was explained in the Bible, there was no problem. Everyone admitted what Linnaeus was still stating in 1740: "There are as many different species as there are different forms created by the infinite Being in the beginning."

The Renaissance passed without any new ideas being put forward in this field. But in the meanwhile, our knowledge of fossils and the earth they are found in was progressing. Ideas were simmering; Francis Bacon, who lived from 1561 to 1626, launched a program "to attempt the metamorphosis of organs and, by varying the species, to investigate how they have multiplied and become diversified."

In 1672, the great zoologist Swammerdam noted that all large animals have similar organs and internal anatomy to little animals, and he suggested that "God created only one animal, diversified into an infinite number of types and species." In 1680, Leibnitz, a philosopher and mathematician, discussed the confusion of the world, and it was his view that when the occasion presented itself, animals could be transformed. In 1719, the French botanist Marchant informed the Academy of Science of the sudden appearance of a new type of mercury in his garden. Today we would call it a mutation.

Along with these serious observers, there were some quite fanciful writers. Maillet, a former consul who had seen fossils in Egypt, wrote a work called *The Telliamed* when he was sixty-three years old, and in it he puts forward theories similar to those of Anaximander and generalizes on them. He suggested that terrestrial animals and birds had come from fishes, who had adapted to their new kind of life. The idea of evolution is here, but only vaguely. There are a lot of gratuitous suppositions among the facts. The tubes in the fins of fish had become bristly and these bristles had become feathers. The little fins under their bellies had become feet. All of this is hardly serious and somewhat senile, but it reads like a present-day science fiction novel. *The Telliamed* was published in 1749.

Two years later, Maupertuis, a well-estabilshed philosopher (he was fifty-three years old), published "Essay on the formation of organized creatures." The book first appeared in Latin. Maupertuis asked whether "the multiplication of the most dissimilar species from two individuals could result," as a consequence of "errors" of hereditary transmission. "Every degree of error would have created a new species, and the infinite variety of animals that we see today would have come from repeated deviations." Thus the hypothesis of evolution was formulated. What sort of reception was it going to receive?

Diderot, always watching for new ideas, welcomed it in 1794 and willingly accepted it. In his work "D'Alembert's Dream," one of his characters, Dr. Bordeu, makes statements that Lamarck, later, would certainly not repudiate: "Needs produce organs."

Miss de Lespinasse exclaimed: "Doctor, are you delirious?"

Bordeu replied: "I have seen two stumps grow into two arms."

Miss de Lespinasse: "You are lying!"

Bordeu: "It is true. And once, when two arms were missing, I saw two armplates grow longer and form two stumps."

Miss de Lespinasse: "This is madness!"

Bordeu: "It is a fact. Imagine whole generations of people with one arm. Imagine their continual efforts, and you will see both sides of the shoulder blade protruding more and more, becoming longer and longer, perhaps even producing fingers at its extremity. It gradually becomes modeled into an arm and a hand. The original anatomy has been altered and perfected from necessity and because of the creature's normal functions. We walk so infrequently, and we work so little; yet we think so much that I fear man will end up by being just a head."

Miss de Lespinasse: "A head, a head. That's not very much. I hope that unbridled galantry . . . . You are making me think of some ridiculous ideas. . . ."

The philosopher Robinet, who was writing between 1761 and 1768, imagined an ideal model from which all living creatures had derived, gradually tending toward the advent of man. He wrote, "How many millions of years or centuries were necessary for the human seed to ripen?" Even today, according to his theory, the seed is continuing to ripen, the model is imperceptibly rising toward new metamorphoses "which will achieve perfection only in future ages." This idea was taken up one hundred eighty years later by Teilhard de Chardin.

Montesquieu favored the idea of evolution. Maupertuis, Diderot, Marchant the botanist—at least one of these three was read by Linnaeus and Buffon. Linnaeus, who in 1740 believed in immutability like everyone else, started casting doubts on it by 1744. In 1762, he frankly put forward the hypothesis that "all species of the same kind originally constituted one and the same species." A mitigated doctrine of evolution limited to within the genus, cautious but logically indefensible, as we have seen. But this is unimportant: Linnaeus was now fifty-five years old, and there are few scientists who are openly willing to adopt new ideas at this age, especially when they did not instigate them. That they do not oppose them is praiseworthy; Linnaeus is to be commended on his open-mindedness.

Even more than Linnaeus, Buffon, a man of the world and a naturalist, had the opportunity to read contemporary philosophers. He was a man very open to general ideas, and he reflected on them and observed.

Even if a new idea, encountered by chance while reading or in conversation, goes unnoticed and is not immediately taken up by the conscious mind, it occasionally will happen that more reading or more thought arouses it and brings it to light. This was how the theory of evolution made its way into Buffon's thought. In different parts of his works, he formulates it, analyzes it with a lot of perspicacity and gives arguments both for and against it. One day, he went so far as to write (thus preceding Darwin), "The species that are the least perfect, the most delicate, the heaviest, the least agile, the least equipped have already disappeared or will disappear in time." But until 1751, he inclined toward the theory of immutability. From 1751 to 1766, he was for the theory of evolution: later his position was not as clear.

As an upholder of the theory of immutability, he had shown the impossibility of the idea of limited evolution. However, he did come to adopt this idea for some time. Then he changed his mind again. If he seems to waver between traditional ideas and the bold new hypothesis, it is primarily because the doctrine of evolution was not supported by any convincing facts and also because Buffon was a prisoner of his age and his position. In 1767, he was sixty years old and at the peak of his career and fame. He was an authority, and people listened to him. As Director of the King's Gardens, the future Museum, it was his role to arbitrate. He did not want to compromise himself in a scandal. Moreover, he had already been condemned by the church and forced to retract his statements by the Sorbonne; he had no desire to start this again.

While Buffon did not take the step partly because he was in too important a position and too well-known, another man did not take it because he wasn't known well enough. Lost in the little town of

Vivarais, Father Giraud-Soulavie explored the countryside very thoroughly, observing strata and collecting fossils. In 1780, he was the first man in the world to show that the land, in its successive strata, contained different characteristic fauna and flora. In addition, he noticed that in the course of time, "for plants and animals alike, nature had multiplied the families, that she had gone about perfecting them more and more, first working on the simplest, then on the more complex." This was the proof that Buffon had needed. But this proof was supplied by a conscientious and sure observer with no preconceived ideas, or at least he had admitted none. In the course of time, he discovered two fundamental laws of the history of life: the increase in the number of types and their gradual complication. And from this he drew no arguments for evolution! His work remained unknown and ignored for more than a century.

Thirty years later, Cuvier, who does not seem to have read his works, discovered the same law of progressive improvement, using completely different material: bone fossils. He distinguished five successive eras: fish, reptiles, the first mammals, mammoths, and present-day animals. But he persistently clung to the immutability theory. He did not look for the reason behind the law he had just proved. He did not attach it to the idea of evolution.

The facts and ideas of the doctrine of evolution are already here in this period of transition, but they are dispersed and fragmented, rather like the incomplete organs wandering around in the dawn of the world, as stated in Empedocles' theory. Will they manage to be linked together?

Yes, by Lamarck, whose life is one of the richest and most exceptional in the history of science.

The son of a nobleman, Lamarck was the last born of eleven children. If birth control had been as popular then as it is today, Jean-Baptiste de Lamarck would not have been born.

He came from a poor family; so he went into the army. In his first battle, the French army was defeated. Lamarck was in command of a small number of troops, and since no order to withdraw reached him, he decided to remain in his position. When night fell and they were finally released, he was congratulated by his superiors. But what was more, he had gained the esteem of his men.

Later, to earn a living, he worked in a bank in Paris. He attended

Jussieu's courses at the Museum, and his first scientific work was the invention of the principle of binary classification or dichotomic keys, so that plant names could easily be found. This system has since been adopted by all authors writing about flora and fauna. He had hoped to be a professor at the Museum, but all positions were filled. While waiting, he collaborated on dictionaries and wasted time in unsuccessful ventures. Finally, at the age of forty-nine, he was appointed to the chair of invertebrate zoology, a position that no one else wanted. He was a botanist, but he passed from the study of plants to his new task, the study of lower animals, and he founded the zoology of these animals. He gave thirty years of his life to this study. To begin with, he fiercely opposed the idea of the theory of evolution. And then at the age of fifty-six, he saw the light. Like Saint Paul on the road to Damascus, his enthusiastic support replaced his fierce opposition. He became an apostle of the new doctrine. In 1800, he exposed his theories; then again in 1809 he published his *Zoological Philosophy*. According to his theory, living creatures evolve by reacting to their environment; their evolution is a product of their own efforts: basically, this is rather like Lamarck's own life.

But were there minds mature enough to understand him? Or were his listeners more attracted to the young Cuvier and the poise and orderliness of his lectures? It seems that Lamarck's students and colleagues respected him as an old man, a hard worker, and a competent zoologist. But they did not share his ideas on evolution. Lamarck knew this, and it disturbed him. Their indifference followed him to his grave. In fact, five years after his death, his remains were thrown into the common grave, like Mozart.

However, other soldiers came forward on the battlefield of ideas. When one man falls, others are there to replace him. In France, Geoffroy Saint-Hilaire defended the ideas of evolution in spite of direct criticism. In England, Erasmus Darwin, grandfather of the great Darwin, was already putting forward the idea of evolution in 1794. In 1796, in Germany, Goethe was comparing skulls of vertebrates and emphasized the idea of a unified plan in nature. In 1819, he wrote: "Every part is modeled according to eternal laws, and every form, even extraordinary forms, contain the original in them. The animal's structure determines its habits, and in turn, the way of life reacts powerfully on all forms. In this way, we see the regularity of progress, which tends to change under pressure from the environment."

But minds were active in other fields of thought. July 1830: revolution broke out in Paris. In Germany, August 2, a friend arrived to see Goethe.

"Well," says the great man, "the volcano has erupted!"

"Yes—the revolution—Charles X."

"We are misunderstanding each other, my good friend. I am not talking about that. I am referring to the debate between Cuvier and Geoffroy Saint-Hilaire at the Academy of Science."

And Goethe continued, "The synthetic method in natural history just inaugurated by Geoffroy can never disappear now."

Goethe had predicted the future accurately, but he was wrong about the present. In that particular case, Geoffroy Saint-Hilaire had taken a dangerous position, and Cuvier did not find it difficult to show that Geoffroy Saint-Hilaire was wrong. Once again, immutability had triumphed.

It has been said that in conflicts, England loses every battle except the last. This holds true for the battle about evolution too.

Charles Darwin (1809-1882), grandson of Erasmus, had traveled around the world from the age of twenty-two to twenty-six. The distribution of plant and animal species in South America and the islands had made him think about the idea of evolution; and by reading Malthus, he perceived the idea of selection. But he waited twenty-one years before publishing this theory, methodically and carefully verifying it first. His personal wealth and a quiet, secluded home gave him the leisure to do this. In 1858, a résumé of his ideas was published. In 1859, his work on the origin of the species appeared. It was like a sudden burst of thunder. Some of the best scientists immediately accepted his theory: Lyell, Hooker, Wallace, Huxley. But the Church was against him. People were whispering, "And what has man descended from? Animals?" There was a storm in the air.

The learned British Association decided to hold a debate. June 30, 1860, at Oxford University, both sides were there ready.

It is rare to see Englishmen lose their composure, but this is what happened on that day. Samuel Wilberforce, Bishop of Oxford, asked

Thomas Huxley if it was through his grandmother or grandfather that he had descended from the monkey. The scandalized old ladies had no time to gasp before Huxley retorted, "I prefer to have a monkey for an ancestor rather than an inconstant, fretful person, who, not content with a doubtful success in his own domain, is now trying, with hollow rhetoric, to obscure questions he knows nothing about."

One old lady fainted.

Darwin had come well documented. He won the debate, and in 1882, he died in honor. In 1885, at the inauguration of his statue, the Archbishop of Canterbury solemnly declared that the doctrine of evolution was not contradictory to the teachings of the Bible. The elderly Huxley leaned over to the man sitting next to him and said, "Soon these good men will be burning us for not going far enough."

On the one hand, Darwin's success is explained by the strength of the facts supporting his theory of evolution and, on the other hand, by the resonance his ideas had in the England of that time, the England of that great era. To these island people, Darwin spoke of the originality of islands and their animals and plants. He spoke of raising animals to the farmers of England. He tried to explain the survival of the species rather than their origin. In this, he followed Malthus. For Darwin, the essential was the struggle for existence, the competition. How could a trading nation like England not be interested in this? It is easy for a nation to agree to a theory that the best are successful, when that nation itself is successful.

Darwin also found eager followers in Germany. Haeckel, the young zoology professor at the University of Jena (Haeckel was thirty-three years old in 1867), created a vast synthesis of the theories of evolution containing both Lamarck's and Darwin's theories. He also did better justice to the many precursors than Darwin had. He posed the problem of evolution on the highest level and dissected it with unparalleled precision. Energetically he fought prejudices arising from a literal interpretation of the Bible. With natural zest, he attacked theologians, noblemen, entomologists, Christians, the bourgeoisie, radical philosophers, so-called zoologists, Negroes, military men, and the infallible Pope.

He had every chance, but by going to extremes, he ruined them. Haeckel was very German, too German. He was criticized for the inevitable errors in his bold essay on man's genealogy. His work came to be considered invalid because of a few details, but this was after a half-century. In fact his work, its racism excepted, still provides us with many topics for thought.

Evolution became solidly founded with Darwin and Haeckel. It naturally went through important developments after them, bearing mainly on methods and causes. These we shall discuss further on. But the time has come to examine the basic principles of the doctrine, since it is our passport into the history of life. Naturally we shall study it in the light of modern ideas and in conformity with the present tendencies of scientific investigation.

One of these present tendencies is to express facts carefully with well-chosen words. For example, here is a frog's egg. Will the creature being hatched from it be the same frog genus, or will it have deviated? The reply is a well-known hereditary fact in the majority of cases. The doctrine of evolution replies in this way, "It is almost certain that there will be no difference or almost no differenre from the frog genus." The theory of immutability suppresses the "almost" of this clear statement and replies, "It is certain that there will be no difference." From this, we can see that the theory of immutability is more rigid and less flexible. The doctrine of evolution, far from being impetuous, is rather more flexible and discreet.

Another important idea in contemporary research is the idea of probability. For example, think about the countless risks of accidents, death, and survival. All insurance policies are based on the estimation of such risks. We shall try to apply these ideas to plant and animal species.

The doctrine of evolution seems to demand a miracle (the word miracle is not used here in a religious sense, only etymologically): that from the embryo of a certain species we get a creature of another species—for example, that from a frog's egg we get a toad. But immutability demands an even greater miracle: that the toad be directly derived from so-called inert material such as carbon dioxide, water, and ammonium salts. But these are all very simple and well-explored molecules. That they or the simpler atoms forming them can organize a structure as complex as a toad, or even a simple toad's egg, is obviously a much more difficult and improbable feat than if the same toad's egg came from a small variation in a frog's egg. The frog's egg is infinitely closer by its properties and chemical composition, comprising the same protein's, and by its structure. The frog's and toad's egg are cousins, and it is much more probable to find an offspring resembling you like a son born from a cousin rather than created from a glass of pure water and fresh air. The obviousness of this appears trivial, but it is this obviousness that we refuse to see if we adhere to the theory of immutability or if we simply shut our eyes to the problem.

But we must admit there was a miracle, and it happened at least once. One day, somewhere in the water, salt molecules, carbon dioxide, and water itself combined to form this structure we call a protein molecule. There are tens, hundreds, or perhaps thousands of atoms, but the miracle happened. The being thus formed is already capable of multiplying and reproducing. In this it resembles a virus already: it lives. This miracle, the formation of a living creature from inert material, is required for only one species, according to the theory of evolution—for the first, for the origin of life. Then we no longer need miracles. A frog's egg is capable of giving a toad. Species derive from each other. The theory of immutability requires as many miracles as there are different species.

But let's accept the theory of immutability and imagine these millions of miracles happened. Now let us see if they can account for the tableau nature presents us today. Most creatures, like our frog, begin from an egg or a seed made of a single cell. Now where will this egg of frog or insect species have the most chance of developing? Not on land where it runs the risk of drying out, but in the water where the environment is much more favorable, more similar to it, and more fitted for the nutritive exchanges. But in nature, proportions are the exact opposite of this probability. By far most of the present-day species, about nine-tenths of them, are not aquatic but terrestrial creatures with their seed developing on land—for example, the hosts of insects and flowering plants.

Let's go back to our probabilities. It already is a great matter of chance for inert molecules to produce an egg of a particular species. An even greater chance is needed to get two eggs, one male and one female.

But this is not our interest. According to the theory of immutability, parasitism is highly improbable: it would take a miracle

Fossil of the Tertiary era: the ancestor of our frogs today.—Photo from *Aus Jahrenmillionen*

to produce a parasite's egg and a much greater miracle for this egg to appear in the appropriate host—dog, horse, or man—ready to lodge it. And contrary to the conjectures of immutability, parasites are numerous in nature. In fact, more than three hundred different kinds have been found in man.

Generally speaking, immutability would have to give us self-sufficient creatures. But then what a lot of creatures would be eliminated: males because they need females; females because they need males; parasites because they need hosts; also all the viviparous animals; seed plants because the seeds need the mother plant in order to ripen; all animals where the young need their mothers' care.

During his South American voyage, some of the observations Darwin made that led him to the theory of evolution he mentioned in a letter to Haeckel: "First, the way in which very closely related species succeed one another and replace one another as we proceed from the north southward down the American continent: secondly, the close relationship between species inhabiting the coastal islands of South America and those species indigenous to that continent: this has greatly surprised me, as has the variety of species inhabiting the Galapagos Archipelago."

These species that replace one another from one place to another, especially when these places are isolated, are called vicarious species. Darwin had noted that in the Galapagos Archipelago, every island, or almost every island, had a particular kind of lizard and that all these species belonged to the same genus. Every island also had one kind of giant tortoise, and only one kind, and this species was special to the island. Only the biggest island, Albemarle, had three species. This led Darwin to believe that there was originally only one species and then the species evolved differently in every island. It was precisely these travel observations that put Darwin on the road to formulating his doctrine of evolution.

And the cases mentioned by Darwin are not exceptions: they are the rule. In Europe, the common hare is replaced toward the North, in Scandinavia and Russia, by a hare that becomes completely white in winter; the two species are not crossed. Toward the south, the same hare is replaced by simple kinds. The Mediterranean hare is smaller, has shorter, looser hair, and shorter, less hairy ears. The Algerian hare is even lighter colored and smaller, half the size of the hare found in the Ile-de-France. And then, in the Sahara, the hares are smaller still and dun colored. Local breeds appear where groups are isolated from each other.

Another example is the Hawaiian Archipelago where the island of Oahu contains, out of four hundred types of snail, almost three hundred of the *achatinella* genus, slow moving little creatures with a pointed shell, not found anywhere else in the world. Each species is strictly located in a ravine, and almost every ravine houses one species. The explanation could be that the island was first colonized by one single species which then became diversified. But, according to the immutability theory, if the various species have appeared independently of each other, why this exceptional abundance of achatinellas? And why on the largest island are there only six or seven, which is much fewer than on Oahu, an island six times smaller?

Why out of 474 species of snails in Jamaica are there eighty *stoastoma,* which is rare elsewhere? For example, Cuba, which is quite close, has only two species of stoastoma, Haiti has only one, and Puerto Rico only one. If the species were scattered by chance, there is no reason for the stoastoma to be concentrated in such large numbers only in the island of Jamaica. It is much more probable that the island originally received only one species of the stoastoma genus and this then developed into numerous species there, rather like a shell exploding into a large number of pieces. Hence the name *explosive genus* has been given to these snails by naturalists. If only all explosives were as harmless!

Lakes in the middle of the land are rather like islands in the middle of the sea. In the solitary lake Baikal, for example, three hundred types of fresh water shrimp can be found, whereas usually rivers or ponds have only about ten.

Other genera are less diversified. But we can get an idea of the global effect by the endemicity rate, that is, the percentage of species indigenous to the lake or island being studied. According to the hypothesis of immutability, species are independent; so those found on an oceanic island were created there as they are, on the spot, or else they were brought there as they are from another land. The first would be endemic and the latter generally are not. Therefore, we should find fewer endemic species the closer the island is to a continent, the more exposed it is to contamination and invasions of species coming from that land. But, as a matter of fact, the actual picture is very different. If we consider seed plants or other easily scattered groups, we find high endemicities for certain islands that are close to other lands: Cuba, 33 per cent; Jamaica, 34 per cent; Haiti, 35 per cent; as opposed to the Kerguelen Islands and Easter Island, 12 per cent, both of which are lost in the middle of the ocean. In round figures, the rate is 11 per cent for the Azores islands, yet 24 per cent for Madeira, which is twice as close to Africa. Once again, the theory of immutability is not valid. Distance is not the only factor to be considered; there is another cause for the irregularity. The theory of evolution offers us two reasons, either of which could have been factors according to the case in question. Genera have exploded; and the older the island, the more species on it have had time to become diversified; so the endemicity must be greater. Statistical support, taken from present geography once again, maintains the validity of the theory of evolution.

So the distribution of creatures over the lands of the earth in the past leads us, like Darwin, to the idea of evolution. In fact, one of the reason he gives in his letter to Haeckel states: "Thirdly, the close relationships linking edentate mammals and present rodents with extinct species of the same families. I will never forget my surprise when I unearthed the remains of a gigantic armadillo, similar to a living armadillo." The armadillo genus, so distinctive with its bony armor, was always found in South America in the recent past, as it still is today. Such a coincidence cannot be explained by the theory of immutability. Following the theory of evolution, it is evident that present-day armadillos derive from the ancient ones, and these burrowing animals that dig holes like rabbits obviously did not cross the sea. This explains why they are found in neither Europe nor Africa.

In ancient geography we find vicarious species as in nature today. Bergeron, the geologist, had noticed differences between the Black Mountain in France, capped today by the sun, and the more rugged, colder mountains of Bohemia. Almost five hundred million years ago, the sea covered both of them, and creatures with a three-lobed body called trilobites, half crayfish and half woodlouse, lived and left their imprints in its slimy bed. But the trilobites of the Black Mountain show differences when compared to those of Bohemia. In one species, for example, we can see a coarser surface, and at the back, a colorful spine instead of a colorless tubercle.

The sea seems to have had a preference for France, linking the Parisian region to the Rhone valley across Burgundy, some one hundred forty million years ago. There were no vineyards then on the banks. But in the waters, one oyster, perhaps an excellent one (who will ever know?): the arched gryphaea. Its thick shells can be found today in our rocks and even in the fields. Its large valve curves slightly above the other valve like an arch: hence its name. The geologists have noted that a certain breed of gryphaea is dominant around Avallon and Semur, while around Mâcon and Lyon another breed is common with a broader shell, not as deep, and with the top of the large valve thinner and not so curved. Where this land today yields good wine, there were formerly oyster beds.

Like a film director, who first shows a long-distance scene of the countryside, then a close-up shot of it, we are also going to change our perspective: from regions and geography, we are passing to the living creatures themselves. Here we can see the unified plan, where resemblance is a sign of relationship.

Haeckel, an informed zoologist, offers the example of hands, or what substitutes for them, in mammals. Man's hand is very like a gorilla's or orangutan's, and they have the same main function: taking. But, "the fact that a dog's forelegs, a seal's and dolphin's pectoral fins, are essentially constructed in the same way is surprising. However, we are more astonished to see the same bones forming a bat's wing, a mole's pick-shaped paw, and the front legs of the platypus, the most imperfect of the mammals," having a duck's bill and laying eggs. The volume and shape of the bones vary from one species to another, but the number and articulations are the same in all, with only a few exceptions. Haeckel concluded, "To what can this amazing conformity, this essential parallelism of internal structure, possibly be attributed? To what, other than a common heredity deriving from common ancestors?"

The same heredity, the same evolution from common ancestors, resolves in a completely natural way one of the problems that has most often intrigued naturalists of yore—the problem of rudimentary organs, too little or too badly formed to function or play a role. Thus, a whole multitude of subterranean animals or creatures living in caves, such as moles, rats, snakes, lizards, amphibians, fish, invertebrates, have their eyes covered by a membrane so that the light cannot enter them.

In the embryos of beef and sheep, there are incisor teeth in the thickness of the bone of the upper jaw. But these incisors never break through, and consequently, they serve no purpose in these animals where only the lower incisors develop. In many whales the jaws of the embryo have teeth, but adult whales have only horny strips of quite different origin. The whale has forward fins, but no rear fins. Instead, right in the muscle, we find only a pair of little bony pieces with no use and quite invisible from the outside.

Flowers also have rudimentary organs in the form of stamen or reduced pistils. In labiate plants, these beautiful aromatic plants, there are usually two pairs of stamens in two receptacles. But sage, which decorates our fields with its violet colored stems, has two stamens and in one receptacle. The other does not develop.

Man himself has rudimentary organs. Let us consider the motor muscles of the external ear. Dogs and donkeys are capable of making the ear move, but not man; yet these muscles do exist. In the corner of the eye, next to the nose, a little crescent-shaped fold is evidence of a third eyelid, well-developed in horses, where it is called a nictitating membrane, and it is also present in birds. The six-week-old human embryo has a tail as long as a dog's of the same age. The vertebrae of the tail remain in the human adult, where they form the coccyx. The tail muscles also persist in adults, useless, small, but quite distinct.

Thus the unified plan, the sign of relationship, can be seen in creatures in their form. It is also manifested, as we have seen, in their functions, hormones, serums, cells, and the molecules themselves, in these proteins that are found in all living creatures and only in them. The shape of the crystals in the red coloring of the blood is comparable in seals and bears, which hints already at human anatomy. The serum most similar to man's is the chimpanzee's. Of all the animals, it is the chimpanzee, too, which is the most susceptible to man's diseases. Like man, it can catch measles, scarlet fever, whooping cough, poliomyelitis, tuberculosis.

Yes, the world of living creatures is really one.

For former naturalists who looked for a purpose, a finality in every detail, this was a scandal. Haeckel has described this scandal in his own way: "What? Tools with no possible use, organic apparatuses which exist and do not function, which are constructed for a given goal, but in reality are incapable of attaining this goal. . . . As there was no way of finding the real explanation for this fact, they had reached the conclusion that the Creator had placed these organs there for the sake of symmetry, or else it was thought . . . that in order to compensate for the absent function, he had wanted to give something ornamental in the vain appearance of organs, rather like the civil employees who, when invited to the Royal Court, put on their uniform adorned with an innocent sword that they never take out of the sheath."

We must forgive Haeckel's irreverence, and admit that he was right. If the rudimentary organs were ornamental, why would they be buried inside the flesh, so well hidden that it needs an anatomist with his scalpel to expose them?

All aspects and all the data just considered were instantaneous, independent of time. Going back to the comparison with the film producer, each one was comparable, not to the film itself, but to one of the fixed images, the succession of which comprises the film. And these led us to the idea of evolution, an unfolding in time. Already these detached views have given us a hint of the plot. Now let us pass to the film itself.

In fact, it is not one film, but two that we are seeing. One is short and rapid, the other is infinitely longer and slower. The first is the development of the individual from egg to adult stage; this is *ontogenesis,* the development of the individual creature; the second is the development of species, or evolution, *phylogenesis,* the development of animal or plant types.

We shall begin with ontogenesis for three reasons. It is shorter. It seems better known, since it takes place right in front of our eyes. Finally, following good evolutionary logic, it precedes phylogenesis, because originally a first creature had to develop before the series of creatures and generations which constitute phylogenesis.

Ontogenesis is the history of life in one individual being, starting from the egg. Let us take as our example the egg of the human species. It is small and simple, less than two-tenths of a millimeter. A thimble could hold a million of them. Its shape is that of a very simple sphere: a membrane around a fundamental mass and, inside, a nucleus as in any normal cell. We were all once like this. And this should be a lesson in humility for us. Every stage of our development determines our life as a man, and it is purely by convention (a rational and useful convention though), that we attach more importance to a reasoning adult. But, strictly speaking, a child is no less a man. The egg itself, in all its minuteness, and all the successive stages, are just as necessary for the development of a man as is his intelligence or his ability to reproduce.

However, our egg is fertilized and it divides, like an amoeba, or unicellular alga. Already, from the time of fertilization, everything the future man will be is contained in it, ready to start in motion, just like a wound-up clock can set off an explosion or a bell. The whole man is there ready to be formed in the fertilized egg which is ten times smaller than a pin head. We have proof of this. While normally two cells arising from the same division remain stuck together and finally give the one and same individual being, it does happen from time to time that they become separated. In this case, we get two individuals, not one. This is how identical twins are formed, and usually they are so alike that it is difficult to tell them apart. They are even alike with regard to likes and dislikes and similar illnesses. But they come from the same egg. Thus, from the egg, the whole creature is already fixed, with regard to material order at least. This is one of the most basic facts and at the same time one of the biggest problems in the history of man and all living creatures.

Then there are the successive stages. After dividing, our unicellular egg becomes a little ball, then a hollow sphere whose wall is made of cells, as in some fresh water algae. Nourished by its contact with the womb, it grows. The cells, similar up until now, begin to differentiate, and in the dorsal region, the future body becomes organized. We can already distinguish three layers of cells, of which one will become the intestine, as in coelenterates. An elongated line running from front to back is the first outline of the nervous system. It is situated in the back, as in chordate creatures—for example the amphioxus, a sort of little fish-shaped worm which is a marine sand-burrower. The original cord is first a canal, then a tube which swells in front to become the cerebrum, while the intermediary layer gives the cranium in front, and the vertebrae at the back, as in fish and all other vertebrates.

Tissues and organs multiply to such an extent that it is no longer possible to follow them all at once. Let us take one organ, the heart. In the beginning, the human embryonic heart is a simple tube as in the amphioxus; then it becomes organized into two compartments, as in fish. In the fourth week, it has three cavities—two auricles and one ventricule—as in frogs and other amphibians. Finally in the second month, it has four cavities like all mammals.

Moreover, the stages that the human egg successively passes through during its development coincide with the transition from simple to complex as seen in our classification of present-day creatures. Schematically, in our mother's womb, we have been amoeba, coelenterate, chordate, fish, amphibian, mammal—in less than two months.

Thus the unified plan is even more striking than we had thought since one single creature, man, in his different states, is sufficient to outline the distinctive features of the living world. For if we consider forms, we do not have the right, as we have seen, to limit ourselves to studying adult animals. All other forms and the various embryonic stages must also be considered. The unified plan that the adult vertebrate had shown is even more informative in embryos. Their resemblances are proof of this. Let us examine four fetuses:

a tortoise fetus, a chicken fetus, a dog fetus, and a human fetus. Their ages are comparable: the fourth week, except for the chicken which is in its fourth day. Their dimensions are the same: about one centimeter. And what an extraordinary resemblance in their shape! The large head; the curved position like someone sleeping; the tail, even on the human fetus; short stumps on both sides, forepaws, and even shorter legs at the back. No trace of fingers or toes yet. But along the back there is the regular subdivision of the vertebrae. And on one side of the head, a little nostril, a big eye, and an ear. Below to the right of the ear, what are these three little buds? A fish embryo has the same thing, and in the fish they become the branchial arches, the gills through which it will breathe in the water. But here? The tortoise, chicken, dog, and man all breathe in the air. Why these slits? So we find useless, rudimentary organs in our own embryo. Embryology teaches us anatomy all over again.

But it tells us even more. The progressive forms from simple to complex that we can see by studying embryology and which are roughly the same anatomical forms of creatures today, as two Germans, Kielmeyer and Meckel, were the first to note, make us wonder how they came to be produced in the past, during geological times. Did they appear in the same order or in a different order?

If we consider fossils, we see groups appearing throughout the ages, going precisely from the simplest to the most complex: the first fish were almost five hundred million years ago; the first amphibians, three hundred seventy million years ago; the first reptiles, three hundred thirty million years ago; the mammals between one hundred eighty and sixty-five million years ago, with the superior mammals that nourish their fetuses with the help of placenta sixty-five million years ago. Thus embryogenesis is a recapitulation of phylogenesis. The progress that has take life hundreds of millions of years to carry out during the long, slow fashioning of the species is accomplished in a few weeks in the development of an individual being. The living creature, like the young dog we pet, or man himself, appears like the most remarkable inheritance machine, and the most apt too at accelerating its creative mechanism billions of times. The embryo gains time. This feverishness that stirs men today, the even greater need for speed, can already be found in the fetus of beetles and earthworms. But we must not delude ourselves and think that this acceleration is miraculous. Each of the successive forms in the development of a complex creature like a dog, crab, or oyster lasts almost as long as in the independent species that they resemble; a few hours for the first divisions of the egg, like unicellular animals; a few days for the swimming larvae of oysters and crabs, as for swimming animals of the same size. The oyster or crab that we eat is formed to a certain extent by placing end to end the lives of smaller, less sophisticated creatures and by adding that duration. A very simple procedure, yet at the same time, very significant, since it points out a fundamental tendency of living creatures: the tendency to last. Perhaps the philosopher could attach man's wish for immortality in part to this.

In any case, the creature tends to live again by going beyond itself. The fish outlives itself by becoming an amphibian, the amphibian by becoming a reptile, and so on. At every step, a new act is added to the play, and the actor extends his role further.

A flexible rule, with some exceptions and abridgements that we shall examine a little later.

The appearance of large groups of vertebrate animals during geological history, in an order going from the simplest to the most complex, is a good example of orthogenesis, or evolution in a straight line. This would be inexplicable in the theory of immutability.

Similar cases can be seen in countless large groups of animal or plant fossils. Let us first consider the remains of plants that lived in the open air. They are recognizable by their microscopic openings which allowed gaseous exchanges across their epidermis, and by their little tubes called vessels, through which the sap traveled. The most ancient known ones date from about four hundred million years ago. The roots date from around four hundred million years ago, and the leaves themselves from around three hundred ninety million years ago. The ovules, the outgrowths where the mother plant harbors the female reproductive cell date from around three hundred seventy million years ago: the seed from around three hundred fifty million years ago. The closing of the ovary, where the seed is hidden, happened between one hundred eighty and one hundred forty million years ago. Here, too, the order is that of gradual anatomical complication, well-explored in plants today.

Similarly, this is so for much smaller groups. About sixty million years ago, the vast western plains of the United States were populated with pretty animals, good at running, as big as poodles, but, above all, grass-eating animals. They had hooves like horses, pigs, or sheep. But on each paw, the middle finger was predominant, unlike sheep and pigs, which have a cloven hoof. There remains the horse, tapir, and rhinoceros which have hooves. But the rhinoceros has a horn, and the tapir a proboscis. The American animal had neither a horn nor a proboscis, as its skull proves. So it came from the horse family. It could also gallop.

Throughout the ages, from fifty million years B.C. up until about five million years B.C., certain layers of earth provide us with the remains of this same family: in one layer, a thousand individuals; in another layer, twenty; in some layers, none. This is part of the risk involved in fossilization. One day, a violent flood catches the animals unaware, kills them, washes them along into a lake or lagoon, and they become buried there under the sediment. Later a geologist will find the remains of the herd. Then many millennia pass, when the animals die in the open, decompose, and do not become fossilized. Or else some are fossilized, but the deposit is then destroyed by erosion.

In spite of so many hazards, the remains of American horses are quite regularly ordered from start to finish, if we confine ourselves to a few well chosen species, the last being the present horse, and not the donkey. Their size increases: it becomes that of a large dog, forty million years ago, and ten million years ago, that of a pony. The side toes have become less and less developed and so, too, have the bones corresponding to the ball of the foot and the palms. Finally there is no trace of them other than two smallish splinters, rudimentary organs with no use on either side of the bone. In the middle, there is one single hoof. The cubitus is knit to the radius. The premolars and molars, very different in the beginning, begin to resemble one another more and more. In the course of time, they have lengthened and become covered with cement. Enamel depressions stand out, showing how they have been worn away.

From one genus of horse to another there is a break, a difference in dimensions and forms. A step is crossed. The progression is like a staircase. But in other groups, it is continuous, a gradually inclining plane. This is particularly true for all animals who used to live in the very environment where their remains have been buried, for example, in the sea or in a lake. The chances were greater here for obtaining a more uniform fossilization. This was the case a few million years ago, in the large lake whose peaceful waters used to extend to the middle of the present basin of the Danube river. A large number of paludinas used to live there. They were a type of mollusk with a coiled shell and convex whorls.

They still frequent lakes and rivers today. In the bottom layers of Lake Levantin, the paludinas are smooth. Then, as we move up the tiered layers of chalk, we see every whorl becoming flatter, then becoming hollow like a sort of band half-way up, and decorated toward the top with a carina that protrudes more and more. Later, still continuing up the series of layers in the lake, a second carina appears, this time toward the base of the whorl, then every carina becomes indented and is covered with tubercles that become more and more pronounced. From one form to another, in the intermediary layers, we find all the transitions, but it is impossible to establish a break anywhere, so the boundary between species cannot be defined, or else it is purely conventional. Here, more than anywhere, the theory of immutability appears invalid.

Fossils, our proof of former life, also confirm the evidence which we have from living creatures in favor of evolution because, from time to time, we discover forms among fossils that are intermediates between present groups; yet these forms have disappeared today. Nevertheless they are related. This strengthens the bonds of the unified plan and makes it even more distinct.

For a long time, we have suspected a relationship between birds and reptiles; both the chicken and the lizard lay eggs. Their initial development is very similar. The chicken's leg is covered with scales like reptiles. The beak and mouth of both can open to an excessive width because of a very complex articulation that allows the upper jaw to move in relation to the cranium. In short, both are swallowers, and they chew very little or not at all. But in spite of so many resemblances, the distance between reptiles and birds seemed great. And then a discovery reduced it by half: the discovery of the archaeopteryx, the oldest known bird—a bird already because of its feathers, but still a reptile by its very long tail with vertebrae, by

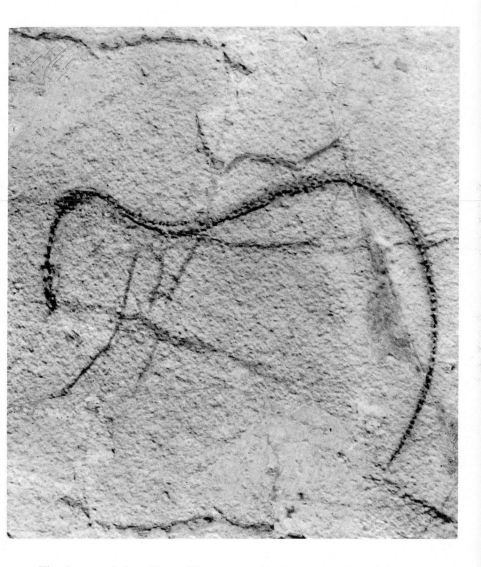

The Leptocephalus, fifty million years old: it became the eel in our rivers.—Document André Bonne

its jaws lined with teeth, and by its front claws. It is believed that it clung to branches between which it could flutter.

Occasionally a discovery will place the missing link between a fossil group and a living group. For a long time, we have known that amphibians once existed, cousins of our frogs today, but differing from them by their long tail, by the number of vertebrae (thirty instead of eight), and by their very protected skull—hence their name stegocephalians. They lived three hundred forty million years ago. The oldest known frogs today date from around one hundred fifty million years ago. But in 1937, in the middle-aged strata (about two hundred million years old) in Madagascar, a French paleontologist, Jean Piveteau, discovered an animal like a frog, but with sixteen vertebrae and a rudimentary tail. Piveteau called it *Protobatrachus,* meaning "the original frog."

In the light of these impressive discoveries, it is hard not to conclude that life has developed from a series of types, derived one from the other. It is not yet possible, however, to deduce frequencies. Among the fossils, are there more intermediate types forming the bridge between two groups, than there are separate types? Only impartial statistics could determine this, but we are uncertain of what characteristics it could be based on. More thought is needed. Research is by no means over yet; there are still many paths to explore.

If it is true, as evolutionists say, that species are derived one from the other, then shouldn't we see new species appearing from time to time?

The number of species presently living is estimated at around four million. Of these a certain number die each year and others are born. Thanks to absolute dates, we know how long the fossil species have lived on the average. These estimations vary between two and eight million years. Let us say an average of four million years. So, if the birth rate of species stays the same today as it was in the past, our population of four million species should witness the birth of only one new species per year, approximately. This sole species will in all likelihood pass unnoticed. In effect, if I find an insect that I think is a new species, who can guarantee me that it didn't exist previously, having escaped the attention of other naturalists?

Yet this improbable occurrence has occasionally happened. On the western European coasts, in the mud by the sea, there is a hardy creeping grass, growing with fine stiff leaves, called *Spartina Townsendi*. It was first noted in 1870 at Southampton, on the coast in England. Then some decades later it was invading the low shores of neighboring countries. Before that, it had never been found in either Europe or America. Other species of the same genus had been studied and described; the flora of England has been thoroughly studied for almost two centuries. *Spartina Townsendi* could not have escaped the attention of former botanists. It is actually a new species. We believe it was formed from a cross between two other species of the same genus, *Spartina Maritima,* known for a long time in Europe, and *Spartina Alterniflora,* recently introduced from America to Europe inadvertently.

We have been able to synthesize certain species. For example, royal nettle is a pretty plant growing in woods or crops, with white and pink flowers, and it does not sting. Extremely easily recognized, it had been described in the eighteenth century by Linnaeus. But it can be obtained by crossing two species of the same genus that have been modified with colchicine, a substance extracted from colchicum (meadow saffron). Artificial stalks are identical to natural stalks; they are maintained through heredity; and between them, they give prolific cross breeds.

Hybridization is not the only reason known for the appearance of new forms. Environmental action can also be influential too. For example, brewer's yeast is normally capable of oxidizing a sugar called glucose. But, if we add a little acriflavine, a yellow coloring agent, then the yeast's budding is changed, and from now on, it yields smaller, slow-growing colonies that can no longer oxidize the glucose. If we isolate the new form and transplant it in a new liquid, it remains stable.

Finally, by carefully observing animal or plant breeding, we can see from time to time an individual of a different breed appear. In the fruit fly, called the drosophila, there are several hundreds of different mutations, for example, red eyes, smaller wings, etc. Each of these mutations is stable; that is, the individuals, crossed between themselves, have produced descendants similar to themselves. The mutation itself is always abrupt, and it appears to occur by chance. We do not know in advance which one will appear.

We were looking for examples of the appearance of new species. Nature and laboratories offer us several possibilities. So we can choose. It was probably the difficulty in choosing that forced Paul Lemoine, in 1936, to write these lines, which no doubt are the last in defense of the theory of immutability. "The theory of evolution is impossible. Basically, in spite of appearances, no one believes in it any more, and without attaching any importance to it, we say *evolution* to mean *chain;* or *more evolved, less evolved* to mean *more perfected, less perfected;* because this is conventional language, permissible and, in fact, almost obligatory in the scientific world. Evolution is a sort of dogma, which priests no longer believe in, but which they maintain for their people. We must have the courage to state this so that the men of the next generation will orientate their research in another direction."

Lemoine was right in voicing uneasiness and inviting research workers to experiment in new directions. But he is wrong in denying evolution. A fact may be true, even if we cannot explain it. We do not know the cause of terrestrial magnetism, but this doesn't stop the magnet needle from pointing north. Similarly, we can hestitate among several mechanisms for explaining the appearance of new species. This is a difficulty that we shall overcome at the right time. But it does not stop species from evolving: their past and present distribution, their very forms, and the embryonic forms have given us much striking evidence. Bearing this in mind, we can now start examining the history of life, starting right from its beginning.

$\mathbf{1}$

The Origin of Life

$\mathbf{1}$

A gigantic problem! If both living and dead plant and animal species are actually derived one from the other, where do they come from? What hand shaped them in the beginning? How? And from what?

Living matter is the contrary of inorganic matter. What did living matter originally arise from? From inorganic matter? If so, how? There are so many differences between living and inorganic matter that we cannot help imagining a vital principle that would have been the cause of it, a principle that one day animated inorganic matter, so that stone became flower, animal, man. But where did this principle begin this act and these acts? In what part of space, in what sea, or on what continent? At what time, what date during the three billion, five hundred million years that earth has existed?

How does science answer these questions and our speculations? Will the answer be similar to its answer for lightning? In ancient times, people believed that it was Jupiter who sent the lightning. Today, we know that it is an electrical discharge, but this does not stop most of us from believing in God as the First Cause. The electrical discharge is one of the second causes, insofar as it can be.

The best information we have comes from fossils, but they are extremely rare in the Pre-Cambrian era, which began around three billion, five hundred million years ago and lasted until about six million years ago. This is all the more reason that we should treat these precious relics with the utmost care. Firstly, here in some slate relics with almost imperceptibly fine grains, we have found bacteria, in the form of little spheres or rods. They are among the simplest creatures, since their cells have no distinct nucleus and they are only about one thousandth of a millimeter wide. They have been found in British Columbia, Montana, Calvados, and even in the iron ore of Minnesota. In Armorica, little lattice-like spheres, one tenth of a millimeter in size, have been discovered.

These are the remains of unicellular animals. Elsewhere, we have found the remains of reefs, several yards thick, in the form of columns, crusts or disks. The most beautiful, called *collenias* are forked trunks, upright and joined together like the pipes of an organ. They have been found in Siberia and North America. At Atar, in Mauretania, planes land on flagstones made of collenias. A cross section of the collenias show growth rings that are found in no other corals. These were probably algae, blue algae perhaps. Even today, certain kinds of blue algae encase themselves in limestone, forming a sort of ball or pancake, as seen in Australia, Morocco, and even in the Seine and Marne rivers in France, where they live at the bottom of the water and have to be dredged out. Today blue algae are still among our most primitive creatures. They are very close to bacteria. Their simple cell has no nucleus. Collenias must have been like this.

In the land around the many lakes of Finland, under the dark forests, or at the edges of the rich grasslands, an anthracite has been extracted from the rock that appears to contain ancient unicellular carbonified algae. Unfortunately, no plant form or imprint can be discerned in it. If there were any, heat and pressure effaced them during the displacements of land that this anicent country subsequently underwent. But not far from there, more distinct remains were found. In some ancient sandstone, little black sacks containing coal, shaped like balls or flattened ovals from two to thirty centimeters long, were found. No apertures, no organization, and no structure could be seen, so that for a long time scientists wondered if these really were the remains of creatures that had lived. Even the name given to these forms, *corycium enigmaticum,* illustrates this doubt. But quite recently, the puzzle was solved, thanks to carbon isotopes 12 and 13. In effect, carbon isotopes 12 and 13 are found in slightly different proportions in organic matter like bones, wood, or charcoal than in inorganic matter like the carbonates of calcareous rocks. *Corycium* is thus classified among the remains of creatures that have lived. But what creatures? Algae, perhaps?

For a long time, *corycium enigmaticum* was the oldest fossil to be dated, being around one billion, four hundred million years old. But recently, something better was found. About two billion years ago in Ontario, near an iron bed, some black silex preserved the impression of two algae, two lower fungi, and one little unicellular creature quite similar to our present-day flagellates that live in water.

There are even older specimens. A Finnish scientist, Rankama, one of our best specialists in earth chemistry, analyzed carbon extracted with difficulty from rocks in Finland dating back two billion, five hundred million years. For carbon 12 and 13, he found proportions that were characteristic of organic matter, the same as in algae today. In Africa, we have been able to date an alga discovered in 1935, thanks to lead isotopes. It was found to be two billion, six hundred forty million years old. This is the present record. But, it was reached so quickly, that we can expect it to be beaten soon, and it must be around three billion, five hundred million years ago that life began, that is to say, after the earth had been formed.

Along with these plant remains from the Pre-Cambrian era, we have also found some animal remains like the lingulella, an elongated shell with two valves, tongue-shaped and very similar to the lingula still found today in the sea. It dates from the latter part of the Pre-Cambrian era. There were creatures already living in the sea at that time. The lingulella and lingula belong to a group of brachiopoda related to sea worms.

In the Pre-Cambrian era, fossils are too rare and there are too many groups missing for us to form an opinion about certain particular absences. Any generalizations could soon be invalidated. But we can draw two conclusions. The fauna and flora of the Pre-Cambrian era are simpler than those that followed them. On an average, they are formed from more primitive groups. Also, they lived in water. There were still no terrestrial animals or terrestrial flora.

Simple plants and animals living in the water—this is the only direct evidence that life has left us of the period closest to its origin. If we want to know a little more, we must use other methods. Starting from life today and its characteristics, we must try to go back into the past, follow the course of life and its variations, like going counter-current up a river toward its source. Previously, man had to rely mainly on his imagination and intuition. Today, he gets more and more support from facts.

We have already seen how in ancient Greece, Empedocles conceived the idea of separate units—limbs, heads, horns, eyes—wandering around and combining by chance into monstrous forms, many of which were then eliminated by life. This was the first suggestion of the idea of natural selection, which was to be taken up again later by Darwin.

In Roman times, Lucretius explained the origin of all species and, in particular, the origin of life by the chance meeting of creatures. He wrote: "I am now returning to the very young world, to the lands that are still soft, to their birth, to what they dared to bring to the shores of light and to trust to the capricious winds.

"In the beginning, the earth brought forth grasses and magnificent foliage around the hills; and across all the plains, the flowery meadows shone with a green color, and trees of all kinds were able to grow tall in the air and to compete in uncontrolled growth. Just as feathers, hair, and bristles are first created on limbs of quadrupeds and on the bodies of birds, so the earth, while just new, produced grasses and shrubs first. Then it created mortal creatures which appeared in thousands of different ways, in thousands of various forms, because the animals could not have fallen from the sky, nor could terrestrial species have come out of the salt water lagoons. So the earth received the well-deserved name of Mother, since everything was created by her. Even now, a host of animals emerge from the earth, formed from rain or the hot sun's rays. So it is not surprising that larger, more numerous creatures developed at a time when they were maturing in the full freshness of the earth and the sky.

"First the race of flying creatures and the various birds left their eggs to be hatched in the springtime, as they still do today. In the summer, the cicadas shed their silky cocoons to go out and search for food and life. It was then that the earth first brought forth the race of mortal creatures."

We could be concerned about the fate of new human beings with no mother. But Lucretius very quickly reassures us on this point. Through its streams, the earth provided them with a juice

similar to milk. He added: "Moreover, the world in its youth was
not yet producing either severe cold, excessive heat, or very strong
winds, because all things grow and become strong at the same pace.[1]

"So once again, this name of Mother that the earth received is
justly preserved, since she created mankind by herself and since, at a
given date, she produced the animals that wander and frolic on the
great mountains, at the same time as she was producing the many
types of birds that fly in the air. But her fertility was not boundless,
so the earth stopped, like a woman who is tired in her old age."

Among the gross errors, we can perceive two ideas that are
probably correct: plants preceded animals, and seeds did not come
from other stars, but from the earth itself. Mercilessly, a statistician
has noted that out of the nine principal ideas stated by Lucretius, six
are false and one is doubtful (the steady march of progress).

In the following centuries, up until the seventeenth, the problem
of the origin of life hardly arose. In Christendom, it was resolved
by the Bible. In the eighteenth century, Diderot was forced to use
many subterfuges to insinuate a different viewpoint: "If faith had
not taught us that animals have come from the Creator's hands, just
as we see them, and if we were allowed to have the slightest doubt
about their beginning and end, would not the philosopher given to
speculation suspect that throughout all eternity the particular elements of the animal world were scattered about and mixed with the
masses of matter, and that these elements managed to combine
because it was possible for this to happen?" Chance meetings: in
short, nothing new in relation to the ideas of antiquity.

In 1845, in his *Cahiers de Jeunesse,* Renan wrote some strange
lines, to which Jean Rostand has drawn our attention. Renan was
amazed by the singularity of Australian fauna that had recently been
discovered. He felt that it was the relic of an older fauna that obviously he could not date at that time because paleontology was not
advanced enough, but his remarks could well be applied to times
very close to the origin of life.

"Yes, what now appears to us as juxtaposed species was linked
by filiation. Species were engendered at a period when they were

[1] A fascinating idea, possibly true in other cases, but not here. In the Pre-
Cambrian era, we have found traces of very great glaciations, intense volcanos,
and deserts where the wind blew unimpeded.

not yet determined (a system that denies classifications is invalid for the present and true for the past), when all were syncretically confused (always the same laws everywhere for the human mind: syncretism, analysis). Yes, at that time, all creatures were brothers. The coupling of different species was much more extensive than now, seeing that the species were much more extensive. From this coupling of dissimilar species, dissimilar creatures were born, and there was a world in chaos with badly defined species. What couldn't I say about what I have on my mind, all I perceive on this point, the history of nature, the genealogy of creatures, everything being engendered, the appearance and analysis of species!"

Renan was right: relationship of species, parallelism between the laws of the human mind and those of the living world. In this latter point, he preceded Thomas Browne, the Marxists, and Teilhard de Chardin. Of Renan's four principal ideas, a statistician finds only one doubtful (coupling) and one false. In reality, the species inhabiting the Cambrian waters five hundred to six hundred million years ago were as well defined as our species. But two or three billion years before that? We are not so sure that Renan was wrong. The question that he so boldly asked is still not answered today.

Philosophers and thinkers, like Renan, can be interested in the origin of life without being accused of boldness. But not naturalists. Thus Ernest Heinrich Haeckel showed courage when he resolutely attacked the problem in 1867. His offensive started from a solid and logical fundamental principle. Throughout the ages, species have evolved, going from simple to complex; so the original creature or creatures must have been simple. In addition, we know that there is parallelism between all creatures living at this very moment and all the creatures that lived during geological times. Each of these two groups forms an extremely diversified mosaic, going from the simplest creature to the most complex, and finally to man. The modern mosaic is complete, spread out before our eyes; but what remains of the ancient one, that of the fossils, is a poor wreck. A host of parts are missing, especially the original ones. In order to restore them, the best models will be the simplest creatures of nature today. Haeckel methodically set out to research them. He literally set out; he traveled and gathered animals from the sea and from fresh water in Norway, the Canary Islands, and Dalmatia. He discovered new amoebae, which are among the simplest microscopic animals; one cell, that's all. But luck was not with him. In 1868, his friend Huxley dredged up a sort of filthy jelly from between four thousand and eight thousand meters deep. Even its nucleus was no longer discernible. He called it *Bathybius Haeckeli,* "the creature from the depths dedicated to Haeckel." Haeckel was very enthusiastic, seeing in it one of his monera, or earliest living creatures. He suggested that the *Bathybius* was possibly formed by spontaneous generation.

Meanwhile, chemists were studying its composition, and oceanographers were searching for it. But let Huxley, ten years later, tell us what happened to his discovery:

"I thought that my young friend *Bathybius* would bring me some honor, but I am sorry to say that with time, it has not kept the promises it first seemed to offer. First, it could never be found where we expected it to be, and this was very bad. In addition, when we did find it, all sorts of stories were associated with it. I am truly sorry to have to confess to you that some scientists have even regretfully claimed that it was nothing more than a gelatinous precipitate of limestone sulfate that had picked up some organic matter as it was falling."

Haeckel's opponents, whom he had created by his harsh attacks, took pleasure in discrediting him. But now, with time, we can appreciate his real merit better. His method was good. His successors adopted it.

Among his monera, he classified not only the unfortunate *Bathybius,* but also genuine amoebae whose nucleus he was unable to find. The coloring agents used at the time would not permit it. In monera he saw "organisms absolutely deprived of organs, composed of a simple chemical compound, yet having the ability to grow, feed, and reproduce." Bacteria and viruses have since confirmed the accuracy of his theories.

A few other naturalists were as bold as Haeckel. All set out from the same principle he did: to look for simple creatures in nature today in order to get an idea of the original beings. This is how Louis Roule, a fish and marine animal specialist perceived them in 1926:

"Eggs floating in sea water (and many present-day creatures lay thousands and sometimes millions of eggs) remind us by their infinite smallness and the countless numbers of what used to be found in the sea in past times. They are not the only reminder. Along with them, deep down in the ocean and even more numerous, there are tiny, minute creatures, invisible to the naked eye, but visible through a microscope. So we can explore them, study them, and we find that the whole organism is reduced to a single cell, an elementary particle of living matter—capable, however, of living, growing, feeding itself, and reproducing."

Today these creatures serve as food for fish and other bigger, stronger creatures, but previously they were alone and made up a world. A powerful world, "maintaining itself by itself, drawing the materials for its growth, constitution, and multiplication from the very environment where it is suspended."

Starting out from this idea, Roule tried to trace back to the very origin. "It is possible that physico-chemical forces may one day be capable of demonstrating how, and under what conditions, life was first able to be formed and throb in the heart of an inanimate environment." In the meanwhile, what is important is "to know the direction taken by this vital movement throughout time and space and to understand its rules and orientation. Its structures are means or actors, but the essential is in what they play, rather than what they are."

An extremely profound thought in which Roule shows himself as a true scientist. Life for him is a game, and so is research.

He ends with this vision of original times. "The sea stretched out like a boundless desert, and there was nowhere to rest one's gaze. However, life existed in this mass. Life was already present; it already had its master qualities, but these were distributed among tiny, minute organisms. Life was preparing to produce what it eventually had to create in later ages, which for us are the past, but which, for it, represented the future. Life was full of these promises for the future, which it was going to realize later. Creative power, the eternal giver of time, was undertaking the work destined to develop in the course of time. As is written in the Bible, the spirit of God was floating on the water."

At the beginning of this century, the gap still persisted between inorganic bodies and living organisms, even the simplest living organisms like amoebae and bacteria, until the discovery of viruses and their strange properties made us reconsider our ideas. The discovery took a long time to come to fruition. In 1893, Iwanowski ascribed a certain disease of tobacco leaves to a filterable virus, a hypothetical living creature. It was so small that it could not be seen, but it could pass through filters capable of holding back bacteria. Then between 1908 and 1915, a French scientist Francois D'Herelle proved that an invisible virus, the bacteriophage, could attack bacteria and destroy them.

A poison diluted one thousand times acts one thousand times less effectively, while a virus, on the other hand, maintains all its strength, spreads, and multiplies: it lives. D'Herelle was a modest man. His works were not known to most of the scientific world until the day the electron microscope was discovered. Now viruses could be seen. They could be photographed.

Viruses are extremely important in the life of man and domestic animals. Poliomyelitis is caused by one virus. Another virus causes hoof-and-mouth disease. They are so small that a new unit of measurement is used in describing them; the millimicron, or one millionth of a millimeter. They are between ten and five hundred millimicrons long. The smallest viruses are not as big as some molecules: for example, those giving the blue color to the blood of lower animals. Their shape, photographed through the electron microscope, is very simple. They are round or rod-shaped, occasionally with a little tail. A shell around an internal mass. Haeckel could hardly have dreamed of anything simpler for the group of organisms he called his monera. Chemically, viruses belong to the great protein family, which constitutes the basic mass of cells and their nucleus and which characteristically contains carbon and nitrogen. Chemists have measured the molecular mass of the proteins of viruses. For small viruses, it is the same as the mass deduced from its dimensions when photographed through the electron microscope. In other words, each little virus is made up of one single molecule. A living creature that is a simple molecule, no matter how big or how small it is—this is something to think about. But it is not all!

Plant leaves often have a pretty mosaic of green and white parts. Chlorophyll has not developed in the white parts. Most of these mosaics are caused by viruses. Stanley, an American who was studying the virus of tobacco mosaic disease, succeeded in obtaining it in a crystalline form. Similarly, the virus causing stunted growth in tomatoes crystallizes into beautiful solid figures with twelve geometric faces. It can be handled and preserved in bottles indefinitely without alteration. It then has all the properties of inert matter. But if we dissolve it again in water and inoculate tomato stalks with it, it causes disease and propagates. It has become a living creature again.

The consequences of this discovery are enormous. One and the same creature, or rather one and the same population, can be alternatively inert or living. Haeckel's dream, one of humanity's oldest dreams, is realized. A bridge has been built between the inert and the living.

But between the two banks of the river, another bridge was built into a different area, that of temperatures. Is there anything less favorable to life than the confines of absolute zero, these 459.72° F that physicists have so much trouble recreating? Chemists tell us that reaction speeds are so slow at those temperatures that it takes a billion years to obtain what we obtain in one hour at laboratory temperature. At those temperatures, life not only becomes slowed down, but stopped, because all matter is frozen, solid, and stiff and cannot participate in chemical changes. Every creature, every seed has become inert matter. And yet, clover, alfalfa and tobacco seeds, bacterial and mold buds, algae, lichens, and mosses, when the French physicist Becquerel exposed them for two hours to this temperature, or to within five thousandths of a degree from it, then brought them back to normal temperature, developed again. The only condition necessary for the experiment to be successful is that the bud has been well dried in advance. The objection has been raised that if the frozen, then reheated bud comes to life again, it is because it was alive before the experiment. Naturally! And so we must conclude that life is distinguishable from inertness, not by its matter, but by its history, its past.

This is like the virus when it crystallizes. Nothing could be simpler or more impressive than the photo of a virus crystal taken through the electron microscope. It shows a pattern of little particles uniformly arranged in rows, like series of parts in a factory, or like gymnasts in a stadium. Each particle is an individual, a molecule. They have to be strictly alike, of the same size and same shape, to be so regularly placed. In a virus population, no traces have been found of little individual particles, baby particles. No growth has been discerned yet. We have not seen any division. The smallest particles do not contain enzymes, these bodies necessary for nutrition. They do not feed, nor do they breathe.

But then we begin to have doubts. Are they really living?

Yes, because they propagate. Poliomyelitis, hoof-and-mouth disease, smallpox, with their sudden epidemics, give us the disastrous proof. The virus does not divide, it multiplies. How? Let us take a bacterial culture and add some bacteriophage viruses. Watch one bacterium. Some bacteriophages approach it and, with a sort of tube forming a syringe, inject themselves into the bacterial cell. Thirty minutes later, the bacterium becomes blurred and is no longer visible. In its place, we find around two hundred bacteriophage viruses. What miracle made them? They were made by a process that no philosopher, no dreamer, no Haeckel had conceived, but which was revealed by the careful study of the various stages. They are a copy formed outside of the creature. In the first stage, from contact with the intruding virus, the bacterial matter has been broken into pieces, as a wall being demolished is reduced to isolated pieces of brick. Then, in the second stage, the bricks are regrouped into little blocks, but this time they are modeled on a new plan, the invader's plan. And about two hundred of these little blocks are formed, and these are the new generation viruses. The first stage lasts about ten minutes, the second stage twenty minutes. The yield is calamitous. More than nine tenths of the bacterial matter is destroyed, and the unused portion becomes mixed with the liquids around it. Wastage begins early in the series of living creatures.

As with animals, plants, and bacteria, there are species of viruses, "races," strains, distinguishable by their shape and properties, just as the different pieces in a game of dominos differ by the markings on them, although their dimensions and shape are the same. Each "race" raised alone is stable, hereditary. In other words, a domino marked two and five will always produce twos and fives. But when we put two different races together, we get mutations. For example, if one of the races is represented by a domino marked six and three and another by a domino marked two and five, by associating the two, we can obtain sixes and twos and fives and threes. It occurs as if each domino, or each virus, were cut in two and as if there were a change of place between the two halves.

A completely similar change can be seen in mutations between breeds of the same animal or plant species—for example between gray and white mice. So this is another reason for considering viruses as living creatures. Moreover, if we were intent on classifying them as inert matter, we would not know where to place the upper limit, because between the largest viruses and the smallest bacteria, around five hundred millimicrons, we know all the stages in size, shape, and properties. There are some creatures that certain scientists call a virus, while others call them bacteria. Any distinct separation would be invalid. Viruses are well connected with the world of living creatures.

Moreover, they strangely help simplify the definition of living creatures as well as clarify it. Respiration of plants and animals used to pose a problem for naturalists. Respiration burns the very matter of the creature, so in a sense it is destroying what life has created, and this automatically implies a contradiction. The little viruses that do not breathe seem much more logical. Moreover, with them nutrition and growth are outside of the definition of life. But their reproduction is not, and it is the only function that viruses retain. Through the viruses, we see that life is reproduction above all. Through them, we see too that reproduction is reduced to its essential: the transformation of foreign matter into similar matter. After disintegrating the bacterium, the virus incorporates the genetic material of the host bacterium into its own structure; it assimilates it. In the virus, reproduction and assimilation become one, while in more complex creatures assimilation is a process acting on food, and reproduction is another process which appears later.

We could compare the virus to a mother-in-law who wants her daughter-in-law to do everything the way she does. Or to use a more philosophical and pleasanter comparison, the virus is the simplest example of an apostolate, since it converts others to itself. However, its apostolate implies a struggle, the breaking of old bonds. These bonds are the bacterial proteins.

All viruses studied up until now can multiply only in cultures of living bacteria or other cells and at their expense. They are parasitic, and by virtue of this, they cannot be the original form of life. But some can stay alive in sewage, which contains a lot of protein material; so it is possible that the first living organisms were types of viruses but living in water containing protein material, where they multiplied.

These speculations become even more plausible when we consider the relationship between viruses and genes. Genes are made up of nucleoproteins. They exist in the cell nucleus and occasionally in the cytoplasm too, and they are responsible for the transmission of hereditary characteristics, like, for example, the gray or white color of mice. Genes divide and multiply from the cell of the embryo to every cell of the creature resulting from it. Occasionally a gene can suddenly vary in the embryo and this produces a new variety, a mutation. So, for example, we find a white mouse appearing from time to time in breeds of gray mice. Another example can be seen in the *datura,* a plant with a thorny fruit and wide leaves, where a smooth-skinned fruit variety with narrow leaves was obtained. A virus can produce exactly the same effect. Genes and viruses have the same effect on the datura. So we are not wrong in thinking that they do show similarities. And just as genes are very important in nature today in controlling the structure of every cell, so we can believe that viruses or similar bodies were very important in the origin of life.

There is no reason to believe that the first living organisms were as complex as our viruses are today. In Haeckel's time, the simplest known form of primitive organism in the living world was the amoeba, measuring twenty to thirty thousand millimicrons. Today it is the virus, measuring only one hundred to two hundred millimicrons. Tomorrow it may be some organism measuring even less.

Here we touch on an ancient controversy about the syntheses of organic matter. For a long time, man had been able to make salts, alloys such as bronze, or oxides like lime: that is, any substance belonging to the mineral world or derived from it. But until the eighteenth century, he had failed in every attempt to make any of the substances characteristic of the living world. Even the simplest substances, like urea or sugar, could not be made from mineral

For the geologist, diatoma often have the shortest life. Some species have lasted only one million years. —Photo P. J. Corson

matter. Some scientists had concluded from this that life is so forceful that man was incapable of equaling it; and, as was their custom, they had turned to the Bible in search of support for their opinion.

But this was misjudging man's force, ascribing to him false limits, and unwisely opposing religion to scientific progress, as future progress showed. In 1828, in the peaceful university town of Gottingen, in Lower Saxony in Germany, a famous chemist named Woehler synthesized urea, an important constituent of urine.

Following him in France, Berthelot succeeded in carrying out a large number of syntheses, including the synthesis of acetylene; and he took enormous pleasure in destroying one of the beliefs of the Christian religion as it was then understood by many people. In reality, Christianity should not have been the point in question. The Bible makes no mention of organic syntheses any more than the Gospel speaks of professional teaching, for example. In the general domain of facts and ideas, science has its own province and so does religion. As far as organic syntheses were concerned, religious men understood them as well as irreligious men. The controversies died down and the scientific work continued.

In the area opened up by Woehler and Berthelot, successes grew bigger every year. Today entire industries are founded on organic syntheses, and several are vastly expanding, for example, the plastic industry. We can make artificial rubber whose molecule has a molecular weight of three hundred thousand. The smallest viruses have a molecular weight of four hundred thousand.

The rubber molecule is much simpler: it is a long elastic chain with short links. But we also know how to make synthesized proteins. No doubt we are still far from making large complex molecules like viruses or molecules capable of reproducing like viruses. But the possibility of doing it is not a fantastic dream. The enigma of the appearance of the first living organisms on earth now more and more seems to be like what Haeckel, and later Roule, intuitively felt it was; namely a chemical problem. We already have an idea of the basic ideas involved. To change mineral molecules such as carbon dioxide, water, methane, or ammonium salts into the organic molecules that make up viruses, plants, and animals, energy is required. This is quite understandable, since the inverse action produced in a wood fire or a gas oven gives off energy in the form of heat. In order for the first organic matter to be formed, it is probable that the energy came, as it does today, either from the sun's rays (ultraviolet or infrared light) or from chemical reactions generating energy.

Thus it is on our globe and not outside it that we must imagine the birth of the first organisms.

We can wonder if life was born on our earth from germs coming from other planets. This is a fascinating four-part question:

1) Does life exist on other planets?
2) If so, could the germs have traveled from them to earth?
3) If they eventually arrived on earth, could they germinate and live here?
4) Is this probability greater than the direct appearance on earth of living matter derived from inert matter?

And these are our present answers to these questions:

1) Yes, life can exist on other planets. Progress in astronomy shows more and more that countless stars have planetary systems, as our sun has. Among these planets, it is probable that there are some situated at a distance where the temperature varies between 0° and 40°C, so that organic matter built on carbon atoms like ours is stable. There are probably several millions of stars like this. And if we knew that other types of living creatures did exist, formed from different materials, built on other atoms, this would increase the possibilities even more. But the only germs that we are concerned with are classical carbonaceous ones.

2) Could these germs have traveled from the planet concerned to our earth? Definitely not nakedly. Ultraviolet rays destroy all living germs, and the sun emits a large number of these rays. Nevertheless, we are alive, and this is because, in the upper atmosphere around the earth, there is a layer of ozone absorbing the ultraviolet rays from the sun and protecting us and all our fellow terrestrial living creatures from them.

It is not impossible that germs could have traveled, between another star and our earth wrapped in some protective material, for example in a meteorite. We know that traces of hydrocarbon similar to those of terrestrial petroleum have been found in the Orgeuil meteorite. We just hope that in the century since it has fallen, some conscientious museum caretaker didn't wipe it with a cloth that had been dipped in gasoline. Mr. Nagy found forms that he describes as organisms in the same meteorite. It is hard to explain how these could have survived in a substance made of iron, that had crystallized at high temperature. But not having seen these organisms, I can neither question their validity, nor reject them. The improbable is possible and it is contrary to the scientific mind to deny something a priori.

3) But if such cosmic germs originating on another planet did reach our earth, could they develop and proliferate here? We have one of two possibilities: either, when they arrived, there were creatures already living on our globe, or else there were not. If there were creatures already living here, the cosmic germs arrived as competitors, but the beings already here had a better chance of being adapted to the terrestrial or marine environment, to its temperature, its salinity, and the amount of oxygen: and so the cosmic germs perished.

If the germs find no living things on earth, what will they eat? If they are carnivorous, they will die; likewise if they are herbivorous. They would have to have been capable of carrying out their own syntheses from carbon dioxide and water and the appropriate mineral salts in the required amounts; or else they absorbed ready-made organic matter which would have to have been already there in the terrestrial waters. All of this, while not very likely, is nevertheless possible.

4) All in all, what was needed was a terrestrial environment ready in advance to receive germs of cosmic origin. But then why wouldn't this terrestrial environment also be ready to receive terrestrial germs just formed there by spontanous generation?

So, we can now conclude that it is probable that life exists on millions of planets; it is unlikely that present terrestrial life is derived from cosmic germs, even if they do occasionally reach our earth. We must remember that the objects Nagy describes from the Orgeuil meteorite differ from known terrestrial beings. Therefore there is no evidence that such beings ever founded a family on earth.

From our present knowledge, it seems more probable that life appeared directly and spontaneously on earth. But from what and how? The first living beings (whether they were on our globe or on others) were the first molecules able to reproduce. They were molecules rich in carbon, nitrogen, and perhaps phosphorous too. They were present in water and able to organize other not too different molecules after their own structure. If we admit that the globe was formed by the assembly of solid particles, then perhaps the original atmosphere was composed of ammonia, methane, and carbon dioxide. By subjecting such a mixture to electrical sparking, Urey, an eminent American scientist, has obtained amino acids, carbon, and nitrogen substances which, by their grouping, gave proteins. On the terrestrial globe, these proteins would have dissolved in water.

A French astronomer, Dauvillier, has proposed another alternative. According to him, the original atmosphere was made of carbon dioxide, nitrogen, and water vapor, with no oxygen or ozone. Thus, ultraviolet rays could pass through it. The pools of water soon formed by condensation would have contained the same substances in solution, as well as ammonium salts. Under these conditions in a laboratory, ultraviolet rays cause syntheses of sugar and amino acids. In nature, the molecules thus formed could have been diffused in water. Those remaining on the surface would soon have been destroyed by the ultraviolet rays themselves, which are both destructive and constructive, like our city planners. But deeper down in the water, the newborn organic molecules were sheltered, because water sufficiently deep absorbs ultraviolet rays. So they could have lived deep down.

Whether one follows Urey's theory or Dauvillier's, the amino acid molecules and others, once born and saved from the danger of rays, could live because there were no living creatures yet to eat them. Thus they managed to unite when they met, if the air and water currents were favorable, if the syntheses and destructive forces permitted it, in the daytime, at dusk, at night, or in the dawn, until the day (or night) when a force appeared that was finally capable of organizing the material swarming around into its own structure. Then the first act of life was accomplished. The first living beings were born.

Thus we see molecules as having the same chance meetings and unions as Empedocles had once conceived for organs. The gulf that many people have seen between inorganic and living matter is being bridged: life managed to emerge from the inert, or living things at least. The simplest atom, the hydrogen atom, was already extremely unstable. And the first living organisms were small and simple like viruses, probably even smaller and simpler.

We shall now trace in broad outline what then became of them.

PART II

FROM CRYSTAL TO MAN

✓

CHAPTER IV

The Stages of Life

✓

At the dawn of the Cambrian period, six hundred million years ago, all the main classes of invertebrates were abounding in the sea. The class with the most species then was the sponges, the simplest multi-cellular organisms, although today they no longer have their past splendor. But let us go forward one hundred fifty million years into the middle of the Silurian period, when the first invasions of land were occurring.

Here a strange spectacle awaits us: bare rocks, sands, and deserts cover what is now Europe, Asia, Africa, and America. The wind is blowing round, coarse grains over the vast plains. Away from the water there is not a tree, no grass, and no animals. The climate, however, is favorable. Moderate rains fall on the temperate zones and below the equator. But there are very few plants and no terrestrial animals, simply because few species seem able to survive in the open air. Life seems restricted to water or to areas bordering the water.

So, let us go closer to the water's edge. Some strange creatures meet our gaze. First, right in the water, there are some slimy animals that swim like cuttlefish and squid today, with their head back and by expelling the water contained in the large sac under their belly. When the sac contracts, a strong jet of water shoots out through the excurrent siphon, propelling the animal in a forward direction if the siphon is pointed backward or in a backward direction if the siphon is pointed forward. This is the principle of jet propulsion. The animal using this siphon four hundred fifty million

101

years before man's appearance resembles our cuttlefish. It differs from it by its straight shell, hence its name, orthocera; others have a coiled or spiral shell. All have tentacles which are used for grasping prey.

Swimming over there are some weird creatures, large marine lice. Two longitudinal grooves extending down their back divide the body into three more or less equal elongated parts or lobes. These animals are trilobites. They have a distinct round head, sometimes a pointed pair of antennae on the head, or sometimes a series of points elegantly curving back. Two enormous eyes guide them when hunting. The body is ringed with segments suggesting a relationship to lobsters or bees. But to which of these two are they related? This is a mystery. On the underside of the body, each of the segments bears a little pair of biramous appendages that help the animal swim or move when it is on the ocean floor.

In contrast to the trilobites, there are other animals that seem to float peacefully under water. There is nothing in nature today that gives us an exact idea of them. They resemble jelly-fish, but their bodies are quite different. Attached to floats are fine, branching stalks, so thin that they resemble pencil marks, hence the name graptolites. Each stalk contains rows of cups or tubes, each one housing a living animal. Little cords within the stalk link the individual organisms together. The graptolite is a colony. It floats slowly with the current, balancing its groups of tiny papillae which capture even more minute organisms such as eggs, larvae, and unicellular algae. The internal cords of the stalks are evidence of its budding, as fibers are evidence of the growth of a tree. They relate the graptolite to a very simple organism found not far from it, forming a crust on the sea floor. It is called an *eocephalodiscus*. It is also a colony of little animals. Each animal has little respiratory slits on the side of its head like those we mentioned for the human embryo. Along the interior of the spine, there is a sort of elastic cord, the notochord, the possible outline of a vertebral column. Are these the distant ancestors of vertebrates?

Yes. And here is precisely one of them, ths type of soft-bodied fish swimming a little higher up in the water: the *jamcytius*. It has a long spindle-shaped body, perfectly adapted for swimming. Its muscles are clamped together in successive blocks from front to

contact with air are modified. Even the front of our eye only stays clean by being moist. If, after four hundred million years, we are still so close to our aquatic origin, not freed from its bonds, we should be able to understand the difficulties of our fellow algae. Hardly had some of them managed to overcome the horrors of the lack of salt and become adapted to fresh water, when they were confronted with dehydration as lake or river levels lowered. Their delicate outer wall, suited to so many exchanges with water, suddenly found itself exposed to the air; if the air environment persisted, they withered and died. So it is not surprising that one of the first adaptations of algae was a hardening, an impermeability of the outer surface, which became impregnated with a substance called chitin, not conducive to exchanges.

We do not really know the physical mechanisms that brought about this transformation, and when we state here, and further on, that the living organism became adapted, we are not implying that it wanted to become adapted, but that if the species had not adapted itself, it could not have survived. Whether willingness played a part or not, and whether a goal was reached or not, are questions that we shall examine in another chapter and not pass any judgment on in advance. The colorful language occasionally used and the expressive comparisons made with man should not delude us.

In plants, impermeability and protection against dessication were also assured by the spores, which are minute reproductive bodies produced by many plants. Four hundred fifty million years ago, spore-bearing plants with thick walls were already living, similar in every way to the aerial spores of mosses and ferns. Remains of them have been discovered in the remarkably well-preserved clay west of Leningrad. At about the same time, or a little later, in Siberia, the first stems able to survive in air appeared. They became abundant, as did leaves, and they were growing in the marshes in the middle of the Devonian period about three hundred seventy-five million years ago.

Spores and stems do not have similar requirements. Moss spores, for example, have only to disseminate until they find a favorable, moist environment where they can germinate by producing filaments from which new mosses will grow. While waiting to germinate, the moss spore has only to survive under the cover of its thin coating of cutin. But the leaf, or stem (in plants with no leaves) are confronted with a different problem: that of assuring exchanges with the air, absorbing carbon dioxide, a precious raw material and necessary source of carbon, and giving off oxygen in compensation. And yet the other, apparently contradictory requirement persists: to reduce water vapor exchanges, resist dessication, and limit evaporation or compensate for it. How did plants manage to resolve this?

Our grasses and trees show us, as do also the ancient plants of the Devonian period. The external surface of the stems and leaves is coated with cutin. It forms an almost impermeable epidermis. But, in places, little surface openings, called stomata allow gaseous exchanges. The are miscroscopic openings distributed in several dozens per square millimeter. But all in all, they occupy hardly one hundredth of the surface area. Their structure is so typical that nothing can be confused with it. The stomata are little narrow openings, whose diameter varies with the action of a pair of crescent-shaped "guard cells" at its mouth. By variations of the internal tension of these guard cells, for example as in dry air, the water volume of the cells decreases and their outer walls curve inward to reduce or close the stomata so that evaporation of the plant's water will either be reduced or ceased.

On the other hand, in moist air, the outer walls of the guard cells curve outward resulting in a larger opening of the stomata, thus permitting greater gaseous exchanges. Yet because the surrounding air is moist, less evaporation occurs. However, it is never completely stopped, and the plant does need fresh supplies of water. This is assured thanks to the wood vessels, elongated cells through which the water can travel. Finally at the base of the plant, either in soil or mud, the water is sometimes absorbed by special organs called roots, and sometimes by the association of fungal filaments with the subterranean parts of plants. In the plants of the Devonian period, the fungal solution is often adopted, but already, we also find true absorbent roots in some species. In any case, thanks to fossilization in silica, stomata and wood vessels have been preserved for us as beautifully as in the cross section of a plant gathered yesterday.

The plants of the Rhynian marshes in Scotland were very strange and beautiful. They had upright stems like rushes, but branched with terminal, oval-shaped sacs where the spores matured; in places, there were little warts in the form of a half-ball, perhaps due to a disease. In the smallest species as in the oldest species, there are no leaves yet. Leaves first appear in the largest species, already several feet high. As a plant grows, if it keeps the same general structure, its volume increases more quickly than the surface area, because the volume is the cube of its dimensions, while the surface area is only the square. Exchanges, which are proportional to its surface area, become inadequate for the volume of the organism. Leaves, by being flat, increase the relative surface area and thus restore the balance. Their appearance in the large plants of the Devonian period may result from this requirement. In any case, the appearance of leaves signifies that the danger of too much evaporation is now averted. The difficulty has been overcome. One great act in the life of plants has just been played. They have succeeded in doing without water, for their upper parts at least. They can now spread their vast foliage to the open air.

And the animals follow. They are the eternal profiteers, living off plants, some directly, and others by eating herbivorous animals. Little insects called collembola, hardly larger than a millimeter, used to live in the Rhynian marshes. They still exist even today. The simplest of all animals, they have three pairs of legs, chewing jaws, but no wings. They live in the ground, where they are very active decomposing vegetal matter and playing a large part in the formation of humus, which is the organic, fertile portion of soil. No doubt they had a similar role in the Devonian marshes, where they helped to form the soil. The earth itself, in an agricultural sense, with its arable land rich in organic matter, is possibly a recent gift of life. Six hundred million years ago when there were no plants or terrestrial creatures, there may not have been any fertile soil yet, or else it was very different from our present soil. Moreover, the desert was very predominant as we have seen.

The success of collembola can be explained in this way. They belong to a group called the articulata, whose essential characteristic is the impregnation of their skin with a rigid, impermeable substance called chitin. A mayfly's wing or a shrimp's carapace gives us a good idea of its consistency. All crustaceans and limuli of the Caribbean

Sea and the Sunda Straits are covered with chitin. Trilobites were definitely chitinized. In all these marine animals, chitin was advantageous in giving their bodies and legs rigid support and, at the same time, more flexibility as well as providing the muscles with a solid point of attachment. Then when the articulata left the water, a new advantage was seen. Their impermeable shell protected them from drying out, like the plastic wrappers covering our cheese today. Plants took many millions of years to conquer the aerial environment; then thanks to their cutin, they triumphed. But articulata, with the help of chitin, could survive in the air right from the beginning. By chance, they were predestined to survive in the air. Their subsequent success has demonstrated this well.

But they shared one problem with all creatures: the problem of respiration and gaseous exchanges. As with plants, the bigger the creature, the harder this becomes to resolve. Since the surface area where these exchanges occur did not grow as quickly as the volume, as we have seen, a compensatory mechanism was required to increase the exchange surface area, either by ramifications or by enlargement. According to the creatures concerned, this occurred either externally or internally. In plants, the enlargement was always external, whether it was in the fronds of algae or the leaves of vascular plants. In animals, the exchange apparatus was split, and two devices were possible. Articulata, breathing in water like crayfish, had external, platelike, protruding structures called gills, attached at the base of the legs. Aerial articulata, such as insects, appearing for the first time in the Devonian lagoons, had the reverse device: indentations, or tubes full of air, called the tracheae, which consist of an extensive system of tubes sending air all through the body, thus avoiding excessive transpiration. Other articulata, like spiders, developed more localized cavities, namely lungs. The tracheae and the lungs can rarely be seen in fossil imprints, but their openings are visible on the sides of the bodies of the first insects three hundred million years ago. They are our first tangible sign of the respiration of animals in the air.

During the same period, other animals too are preparing to confront the air: for example, vertebrates, then in the prime of their first expansion. They all still have the form of fish and live in water. Almost all have respiratory slits, through which they can breathe dissolved gas. But in addition, two of them have very important organs: two internal nostrils, openings through which the nose communicates with the throat. One of them is a coelacanth belonging to the Latimeria family, the living fossil of the Comoro Islands. The other is classified as Dipnoi, a class of fish able to breathe by two methods, in water and in air. Dipnoi too, were first known as fossils, and then they were found living in Australian lakes. During the rainy season, the lakes are full, so the dipnoi breathes in water through its slitlike gills. When the dry season comes, and the lakes are dried up, the fish lies in the mud and can breathe air with the aid of its lung. But then, it breathes through its nose; hence the need for internal nostrils. It is probable that in the ancient Devonian marshes in Scotland, the same nostrils played the same role; and in fact, in the rocks where their imprints are preserved, we have found traces of rippling and a fossil soil, which are indications of a shallow lake alternately full or dry, according to the season.

Elsewhere, and since the beginning of the Devonian period, the bottoms of lakes show foot imprints indicating the existence of a four-footed creature, no doubt an amphibian. But the creature itself has vanished, leaving no other trace, and we must wait until the very end of the Devonian period to discover the skeleton of the first amphibian animal. It is a strange animal, a sort of flat-bodied, wedge-headed salamander, low on its limbs, with legs built similarly to ours, but shorter and stockier. In spite of its legs, the animal had to live mainly in water, judging by its lateral line, the fine row of sense organs, still visible along the side of our fish. No doubt the first amphibians occasionally did walk on the sea floor, but usually they had to swim, and, from time to time, they would point their nose up to the surface and take a breath of fresh air. At the same period, in other seas, other vertebrates and other articulata were continuing to breathe peacefully in the water just as their descendants do today. Thus we wonder how the living world would have evolved if there had been no temporary lakes occasionally drying up. For respiration in the air to be accomplished, these harsh conditions, unfavorable to living creatures, were necessary. In the history of life, there must be difficulties, and there must be a struggle with the environment or surroundings for some creatures to triumph and progress.

This is often true, too, in the history of man.

How beautiful and nimble the fish of three hundred seventy-five million years ago were in the lagoons and in the sea. In contrast with their ancestor *Jamoytius,* who had no limbs, they already have many varieties of limbs. Some have one pair, some have two pairs, though others still have none at all. In this fish, the limb is a paddle; in that fish, it is a simple outgrowth; in this fish, it is an articulated fin; but in yet another fish, the fin is all one piece. In the ancestor of the Latimeria, there are bones forecasting a shoulder articulation. As in the vast majority of fish today, all these fins probably served as stabilizers, and the animal moved forward by undulating its body rather than by moving its fins.

Variety has also developed in methods of eating. Some fish follow the Jamoytius tradition. They still have no jaws, but with their large pharynx, they swallow fine particles of food brought to them by the respiratory current. Even today, this is how their cousins, the primitive chordates, eat. All the other fish, the true fish, have jaws. Think about someone with a deformed face, or even old people with no teeth, and try to understand the tremendous advantage of having a mouth that can bite and teeth that can hold food, bite it, and chew it. The dipnoi in the Devonian lagoons had their palates lined with rough teeth, which probably allowed them to chew algae. Other fish had sharp tooth-plates. The ancestors of the Latimeria had pointed teeth. They were probably carnivorous.

Vertebrates were not the first animals to profit from jaws. Trilobites preceded them in this respect. Their great individuality and originality, distinguishing them from all other animals and helping in future progress, was in having their central nervous axis, brain, and spinal column situated dorsally, behind the alimentary tract. Arranged thus, contact with the alimentary organs was more difficult. But on the other hand, the brain and spinal cord were more closely related to the sense organs and musculature. Our ancestors, the vertebrates, by their very structure are a cerebrally orientated organism, as opposed to an organism directed by its digestive functions.

Since the dawn of the Devonian period, their general orientation has been acquired. And two strategies can be seen in their relations with other animals. Both are strategies used in all wars, all struggles, and all sports: position and movement. We can see the strategy of position from the protective armor plates around the neck and down

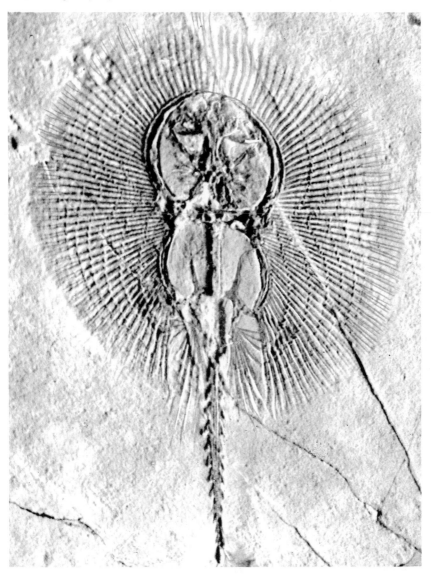

The Mediterranean Sea flowed directly into the Indian Ocean when this long-tailed ray (Cyclobatis) was living eighty million years ago.— Document André Bonne

the front of the body. Made of strong, bony plates, well linked together, they protect the fish against its enemies. But what enemies? Perhaps the bizarre gigantostraceans, a type of gigantic lobster, six or seven feet long, with awesome claws, related to the limulus found today in the Sunda Straits. In any case, the armor-plating of the Devonian fish covers only the front of the body, leaving the back half or two thirds free, which is the most effective arrangement for swimming by undulatory movements. Sometimes the armor-plating is even reduced to a dorsal shield. The fish is structured more for movement than for defense, as can be observed in fish with no armor-plating, for example, the ancestors of the Latimeria, with their tapered spindle form perfectly adapted to produce minimum resistance when moving through the water and maximum power from its tail when swimming fast. Structured thus, fish travel like arrows.

Let us leave the Devonian waters and move to the dampness of the *Carboniferous* forest, seventy-five million years later. In the swamps half-filled with water, there is luxuriant vegetation. Some trees are about one hundred fifty feet high. There are tall trunks terminating in bunches of leaves and others opening out into great crowns of foliage. There are stalks spread in clumps like bamboo, with creepers surrounding them in vast wreaths. The trunks are decorated like fine metal work with imprints that are the scars of fallen leaves. These are either arranged in vertical rows or twined around the trunks in graceful, regular spirals. The foliage is very elegant, with the same fine structure that ferns have, or it may have small scales, or else it is in beautiful, long, tonguelike strips.

What a difference between this and the pitiful foliage of the Devonian marshes, seventy-five million years earlier! Plants have grown, and the species have become diversified. But better still, new organs have appeared. Let us take a closer look at the reproductive organs. First, here are some sacs where the spores of ferns and related plants develop. They rupture, and the spores or tiny seeds are blown away by the wind and scattered over the ground. Perhaps one of them will germinate there. If all goes well and they fall on ground where there is enough water or dew, a tiny blade will appear where cells will be formed. The union of these cells produces the embryo from which the new plant develops.

But in other species with a different type of foliage, we can observe swollen organs like natural tumors, instead of spore sacs. In these plants, the female spore remains in the one place. The mother plant, from its contact with this spore, has reacted by forming a gall, just as it would in contact with a foreign body or parasite. The cells multiply and the tissue swells. Thus the ovule is formed. The female spore remains inside the mother plant, germinating there and protected and nourished by her. The male spore, or pollen, dispersed by the wind, comes to rest beside the female spore and germinates there. Both of these spores will produce reproductive cells, and fertilization will take place in the mother plant. Then the ovule will drop, and the embryo that has formed inside it will develop and give a new plant.

Is this method advantageous? This is debatable. We have observed that spore-bearing plants leave the mother plant and produce their young away from her. On the other hand, plants with ovules do no traveling. Reproduction occurs within the parental plant. Propagation of the species away from the parental plant is more difficult.

The advantage of reproduction within the parent plant can be seen at the end of the Carboniferous period when a new threshold is crossed. From its contact with the mother plant, the ovule receives a plentiful supply of food and can build up reserves. The seed is established from now on. Once it becomes detached from the mother plant, it can wait for a suitable time to germinate, and, above all, the young plant that develops from it will have nourishment on hand from its own reserves to be utilized during its initial growth, which is the critical period in the life of all organisms. Henceforth, the preservation of the species has been greatly facilitated. Plants with ovules may have to live under the protection of the parent plant, but their young derive an enormous benefit from this.

In the history of life and even in the history of man, the seed is a precedent. The transition from the egg to the embryo, in effect, extends the contact that the new organism has with those that engendered it. The embryo derives a greater profit from remaining in contact with the parent. Its young life lasts longer now, but has been facilitated. Thus the life of the human foetus in the womb of its mother and then later the education of the child and young adult are part of a very old tradition of living creatures.

Although plants were the first to profit from this innovation, they were greatly surpassed in other respects.

In the Carboniferous forest, they are content to disperse their spores passively, and later their seeds. In the same shady forest, animals are achieving more in the area of action and movement. They acquire wings, and they can fly. This achievement, three hundred million years before man, was not accomplished by one of his related species, namely a vertebrate, but by a completely different class of animals who had already taken a distinct step forward from their preceding stage in that they were the first to adapt themselves to the aerial environment. These are the articulata or insects. See them flying from leaf to leaf and branch to branch. Look at the gracious dragonfly with diaphanous wings. Its thorax and abdomen, which for a long time bore legs on the underside, now have wings on the upper side. This is a recent acquisition. The young, when hatched, do not have any, just like their ancestors. Then, each time the animal molts, larger wings sprout: first outlines, then stumps, and later the wings themselves. As the thorax consists of three segments, some Carboniferous insects have three pairs of wings, the first pair being smaller. But most insects have only two pairs, like insects today. Striated muscles contracting rapidly (more rapidly than our striated muscle) assure the necessary frenzied beating. Their great success came very quickly. Two hundred ninety million years ago, a giant dragonfly had a record wing span of twenty-six inches.

In comparison with insects, the vertebrates are slow in developing. They are still confronted with problems of breathing and walking. Here in the shady swamps, there are fish with silhouettes similar to present-day forms. Perhaps they had difficulty breathing in the badly aerated water. Hollow tubes, the precursors of lungs, leave the throat or respiratory cavity. The throat itself is used for breathing and sometimes even the stomach or the intestine. The whole surface of the body can be used too, on condition that the skin is thin enough. Other vertebrates surface and open their nostrils at water level to breathe in fresh air, like frogs today. Some of these are fish of course, but there are also quadrupeds: amphibians with a glossy skin. Although they have already existed for seventy-five million years, they still prefer to live in the water. Using their short legs, they can, if necessary, hoist themselves on to the river bank. On a rock in Indiana, we have found the imprint of their five toes, bigger than those of a large dog. So the fin stage has definitely passed. What instinct led amphibians to leave the aquatic environment and venture into the open air? Could it have been the seasonal drying up of the lakes? When this happened, the various vertebrates adopted one or other of the two possible solutions, either position or movement. While dipnoid fish stayed where they were and sank into the mud to wait for the rain, amphibians set out to find more constant lakes. Perhaps on the way, they found tasty food, new to them, such as sweet centipedes, spicy spiders, and tender ferns. Thus without thinking, they became accustomed to the hot sun's rays and the refreshing breezes.

Along with them, heavy, thick-set reptiles, usually frequenting the water, were already living. Their jaws were more complex. Thanks to their long necks, the head, separated from the body, had much more liberty and so was better able to look for prey and vary its strategies of attack and defense.

The end of the Carboniferous period and the following Permian period seem to have been witnesses to a major crisis, at least as far as climate and the living world are concerned. If we take a look at the earth a little later in the Triassic period, about two hundred ten million years ago, we see that the picture has changed. Instead of the luxuriant, Carboniferous swamps, there is now desert or semi-desert almost everywhere, as seen in Arizona or Turkestan. From Catalonia to Silesia, from Sweden to the Vosges mountains and the South of France, there are vast sand-covered areas where the wind blows as it wishes, forming round coarse grains. From time to time, there are great storms, and torrential rains erode the country. Mountains are attacked, and, eroded at their base, they gradually recede. At their feet, the floods stretch out their debris; sand, gravel, and sometimes silt or mud. Enormous deposits accumulate and become consolidated. Thus the red sandstone of the Vosges Mountains is formed and likewise other sandstone in Africa, Australia, and America.

Rivers are shallow and not very wide and frequently change courses like the wadies at the foot of the Atlas mountains in the Sahara, Africa. Sudden floods tear up strips of mud, depositing them further along in the sand, in the form of soft silt. Voltzias grow near the low river banks. They are like little araucarias, resembling bushes rather than trees. Their leaves or "needles" are very resistant to drying out. Not far from them are ferns and equisetums, commonly known as horsetails, with their elegant plumes. An important fact to note is that the same flooding caught all the plants more or less at the same stage of development. The sandstone beds that we can study from quarry to quarry are proof of this. One shows voltzia branches with their male flowers; another has intact seeds that are germinating; and yet another has the very young plants. Thus, each year, the flooding occurred at a different part of the season.

Animals frequent the rare bushes and the rare persistent pools of water. There are cockroaches, dragonflies, and scorpions. Quadrupeds, reptiles, or amphibians move in the mud and leave imprints of their extremities there. In the pools of water, after the rain, sometimes fresh water mussels and other fresh and salt water mollusks are born. Then, another year, crustaceans are found. Soon the pond dries up, and all the creatures, born together, die together, in more or less the same stage of development, as little shells, young larvae, or adult individuals. There are few species at the same time, but each species has a lot of individuals that are often young. This is one of the characteristics of the harsh environment of the Triassic period, and is likewise a characteristic of today.

Not only species, but also the countryside has changed since the Carboniferous period. Animal and plants groups are no longer the same. We could search in vain for plants with ovules and plants with fernlike leaves, for the beautiful trees with long, tongue-shaped leaves, and the fearful gigantostraceans. Similarly, in the fresh water, armor-plated fish have disappeared. There are a few ancestors of both the Latimeria and our present-day bony fish remaining. But they are of different species. New groups have appeared: for example, in Madagascar, Jean Piveteau discovered the *Protobatrachus,* which is the ancestor of our frogs, and which is still slightly awkward both on land and in water. Look at these amphibians. They are labyrinthodonts, whose infolded enamel in their teeth makes extremely complicated patterns. They are found in countries as far apart as Russia and South America. And here are reptiles, whose jaw is a forerunner of the jaws of mammals, with three varieties of teeth: incisors in front, tusklike canines, and molars with three points at the back. Their expressive countenance is in contrast to the impassive outward appearance other reptiles always show. For the first time, facial muscles appear, and with them come the first grimaces, but also perhaps the first smiles, and the first examples of facial beauty. Between true reptiles and true mammals, there is a whole series of transitions and links that occurred in Central Asia from two hundred fifty-five million years ago. The insect world has become more prolific. In the Carboniferous period they all had chewing jaws, like crickets or dragonflies. Now, they can suck and sting. In the Carboniferous period, the young insect reached adulthood only through a series of gradual transitions. Now, many insects have sudden metamorphoses like so many present-day insects.

There is also an enormous change in sea life. The slender graptolites floating in the water are extinct and so are the swimming or burrowing trilobites. Irreparably extinct are the races that built the ancient coral reefs. These were ancient cuplike sponges, compound polyps, and horn polyps with four main partitions. Reefs are still being built, but they are now being built from polyps with six main partitions. Of the eight main classes of sea urchins, starfishes and related animals, two classes are extinct, namely the cystoids. But sea urchins are proliferating and becoming diversified.

The sea still contains beautiful mollusks with tentacles, swimming by propulsion. But let us look at them more closely. Here are some ammonites with coiled shells. The interior partitions that subdivide the shell are all cockled and scalloped, especially at the edges. The suture line, formed by the junction of the stalk with the shell wall, has strange arabesques that are characteristic of genera and species. Some sinuosities or serrated sutures as in the sutures of our cranial bones are understandable. They make the junctions more firmly and solidly knit together. But what is the purpose of so many embellishments, so many strokes, and so many strange zigzags? A military man would say, "Don't try to understand." But we are trying—and we do not understand.

The curtain has fallen on the problems of the Triassic period. Let us raise it again around one hundred million years B.C. in the Cretaceous period. Once again, the scenery has changed. Beautiful forests cover Europe, the Americas, and Greenland too. Beneath their thick foliage, the ground is well sheltered from the wind. Deserts are rare. Rivers and the sea leisurely build up sand and sediment. The reign of dense forests had already begun long before in the Jurassic period, about one hundred eighty million years B.C., but never had it been so extensive. Before three hundred seventy-five million years B.C., deserts had prevailed with rare terrestrial plants inhabiting the swamps. Later, we do not know to what extent there was vegetation on the earth. Carboniferous plants show almost all the characteristics of our marsh plants. In the Triassic period, some plants with exposed seeds were well adjusted to the dryness. The sandstone in the Vosges mountains, containing voltzia remains, is a good example of this. Vegetation was then probably limited to strips along some rivers or rare, scattered bushes, as in Australia or New Mexico today. It is only since one hundred eighty million years B.C., that is, since the Jurassic and Cretaceous periods, that the extension of dense forests can be attested to.

At the beginning of the Cretaceous period, seed plants made further progress. Until now, the ovule had been exposed, and when the time came, the pollen fell directly onto it, as it still does today with the pines and araucarias. But henceforth, some plants have their ovules enclosed in an ovary, which is connected to a stalk or style. Pollen grains fall onto the top of the style, where they germinate before fertilizing the ovule. The ovule will become an embryo within the ovary. The ovary becomes a fruit, and thus we find pips inside an apple, or peas inside a pod. Since the Cretaceous period, while the ovary is young, it is surrounded by sepal leaves and a whorl of usually brightly colored petals. The flower has been born.

Now let us travel across the Atlantic to Greenland, not too far from the North Pole. Here in the lush undergrowth of ferns, we find magnolia trees, with enormous flowers, sumptuous sequoia trees, laurel trees, and camphor trees. And here, in stone, we have the imprints of their leaves, even down to the fruit of the plane tree, with its familiar prickly balls. The climate is hot, similar to the climate in the south of France and Sicily. Even in Europe, palms and screw pines are growing.

As flowers are appearing, so are insects that live off flowers, like the first butterflies, the first bees, and also the wasps. All these insects have abrupt metamorphoses, following a tradition that is now well established. At the bottom of the corolla, at the base of the petals, butterflies and bees are eating the nectar. At the same time, their body becomes coated with pollen and they carry it from flower to flower, thus taking over the role that up until now had been held solely by the wind. They could not live without the flowers, but without them, flowers would remain sterile. Thus, the evolution of life is not all struggle.

In the Cretaceous period, the vertebrates produce an innovation. The first true mammals appear. No matter how diversified their way of life may be, they have one common characteristic. They suckle their young.

But in the Cretaceous countryside, mammalian animals are still poor parents. The class that is dominant by the variety of its species, their size and numbers, is reptilian. There are tortoises and crocodiles. A lizard called the mosasaur is forty-five feet long.

Other reptiles abound on the land that has emerged. Their enormous size and their weird structure have earned them the name dinosaurs, meaning terrible lizards. Here, in their midst, there are iguanodons, over fifteen feet high, standing up on their hind legs. They inhabit the fields, where, using their teeth like those of the American iguanas, they graze on the thick grass.

The iguanodons have left their footprints in clay. We have had no trouble in reconstructing the way they walked or trotted. At rest, both legs were firmly placed on the ground, and at the back, the strong tail was stretched out along the ground so that the animal stood firmly like a tripod. A little later, in America, we find the duck-bill trachodon, with the gait of a dancer—or an ambassador—but its feet are webbed. Its head is shaped like a violin, and the trachodon is known as a water-loving reptile. The stegosaur has feet like an elephant. Its small head, mounted on a short neck, is carried close to the ground. It has a strongly arched back and a flat tail with four spikes located near the end. But the most characteristic feature of the stegosaurus is the double row of triangular bony plates which run down the middle of the creature's back. What is the purpose of this strange armor plate? Does it frighten its enemies? The jaws of the stegosaurus are too small for it to attack other animals. The whole frightening aspect of this creature comes from its massiveness, and especially its enormous hindquarters. Its brain is minute, much smaller than the enlargement of its spinal cord in the hip region. The brain probably weighs only about four ounces, whereas the over-all body weight is about ten tons.

On the other hand, the triceratops has a sort of bony, three-horned helmet, with a flaring bony collar extending back over the neck and shoulders protecting them like a hood. It is massively built like a rhinoceros, and it measures between twenty and thirty feet long. The ankylosaurus is a dinosaur anchored in a heavy bony shieldlike covering that protects the whole body, including the eyes and nostrils. Modern tank manufacturers have invented nothing new.

All this order of dinosaurs (the Orinthischia) have a pelvic structure similar to that of birds, although we do not really know why. The other order of dinosaurs (the Saurischia) have a pelvic girdle like that of the lizard. Saurischians are particularly abundant in the Jurassic period, for example when the diplodocus is living. It measures over eighty feet in length, yet its brain is no bigger than a hen's egg. But the records for size are broken in the Cretaceous period with the atlantosaur and the gigantosaur, measuring about one hundred fifty feet long. All these monsters walk on four short but stocky legs. The enormous, long body tapers into a long, thick tail. But most unusual of all is the tiny skull perched on top of a long, snakelike neck. Their teeth are the teeth of harmless, herbivorous animals. They spend a lot of time in the water, which helps in supporting their great weight, and they seem to have dug up soft, succulent plant material from the edges of the marshes to feed on.

But now, we can see their carnivorous cousins, moving only on their hind legs, and grasping their victims in the sharp claws of their forefeet before tearing them to pieces with their sharp teeth. Look at the agile mock-ostrich; the heavy horned ceratosaurus, twenty-five feet long; the tyrannosaurus, meaning "tyrant lizard," king of the flesh-eating dinosaurs, forty-seven feet long, with an enormous head, powerful jaws, and cruel double-edged teeth shaped like daggers.

Such is the strange world of dinosaurs, the largest and most terrible animals that walked the earth and the shores. Now let us go out into the ocean. Here we can see more unusual creatures, with tapered bodies, well adapted for swimming. These too are reptiles. Their limbs and their craniums are our evidence. Here is the ichthyosaurus, or "fish lizard," plump and with a large head resembling a whale's. And here is a descendant of the plesiosaurus, flatter and with a shorter tail. From time to time, it lifts its strange, little head, set on a long neck, out of the water.

In the air, we can hear the slow, majestic sound of flapping wings. Reptiles, in turn, have conquered the air, and to a large extent, they have surpassed the insects. The pteranodon has a wing span of twenty feet. This record is broken only by airplanes.

Birds appeared just before the Cretaceous period. First was the archeopteryx, which was little more than a reptile with a long feathered tail. In the Cretaceous period the ichthyornis is flying, as big as a pigeon, but with teeth. It dives into the sea to feast on fish. The Hesperonis, a flightless sea bird found in western parts of the United States, more than four feet long, swims like a penguin with the help of its webbed feet. It has only vestiges of wings and seizes fish with its conical teeth.

The same surprising variety of forms can be seen, too, among the creatures inhabiting the sea. For example, hosts of ammonites throng the shallow seas; some are coiled in spirals, others in helixes, and others are limp and uncoiled. There are belemnites and mollusks too, but with ten tentacles. Their shells end in a large point like the profile of a bullet. They swim by propulsion, moving forward as if drilling through the water. Near the surface, fixed firm, live the rudistids, a sort of oyster with thick inner walls, and a lower valve that is distorted and cone-shaped. They build enormous bulky reefs, the ruins of which can still be found encircling the top of the mountains in Provence in France.

But the last act is approaching. The main characters are dying. With the end of the Cretaceous period, there are no more rudistids, belemnites, ammonites, birds with teeth, flying reptiles, plesiosaurs, fish lizards or dinosaurs. Species and entire classes disappear. Why? Rudistids are rivaled by corals as reef builders. Ammonites and belemnites are rivaled by fish and possibly sea snails, which are now becoming abundant. Flying reptiles are rivaled by birds. But what about the swimming reptiles? Twenty million years must pass before their replacements—whales, seals, and walruses—appear. And what about the dinosaurs? We have found their eggs, as big as pigeons' eggs, lying in nests on the ground. Were they taken from the nest and eaten by mammals, birds, or reptiles? The large animals are less numerous, therefore they are more easily exterminated. But did the individuals of the same dinosaurian species all die at the same time, at the hand of the same rivals, or the same disease? Or was their exaggerated growth and bizarre shape the effect of hormonal imbalance? Or should we be like the poets and invoke some mysterious impoverishment of the species? But the giant reptiles took twenty million years to die. This is a long time to be dying . . .

If we take a closer look and bear in mind the absolute dates, we must change our tune. All the creatures condemned to death from the Cretaceous period did not die at the same time. The lizard fish disappeared about eighty-five million years B.C.; plesiosaurs and flying reptiles disappeared about eighty million years B.C.; the large sea snakes disappeared about seventy-five million years B.C.; ammonites about seventy million years B.C.; and the giant turtles and champosaurs about sixty-five million years B.C. The plant world went through this same period without drastic changes, but it had undergone a renewal one hundred thirty-five million years B.C. Thus each group has its crises and its prime. And how could we hope to unravel the causes with any degree of certainty? With very few exceptions, we barely know any of the diseases with which they could have been afflicted. Before trying to explain all the developments and disappearances in the history of life, let us first try to establish them.

The development which begins asserting itself sixty-five million years ago in the Tertiary period is the development of mammals, animals with a protective covering of hair, who nourish their young on milk. Until then, animals were laying eggs, or else like kangaroos today, the young were born in a very small, immature state like fetuses. Then they crawled into a pouch on their mother's belly, feeding there at their mother's udder until large enough to go out on their own. New progress can be seen since the beginning of the

This pterodactyl, a flying reptile whose wing was attached to the end of one enormously developed digit, fell into the Solenhofen marshes in Bavaria one hundred forty million years ago.—Document André Bonne

Tertiary period. Inside the mother's womb, the young embryo forms a placenta, which permits exchanges between its own blood and its mother's blood. Thus, well-fed and well-protected, it can develop in a leisurely way. It is already considerably developed by the time it is born. For example, only a few hours after being born, a young lamb is bounding about. Care for the young and parental help have reached a new level of perfection here. Placental mammals have it in their blood in the most literal sense of the expression.

At the same time, their brain and intellectual aptitudes are being perfected. Compared with reptiles, mammals have a very large forebrain. During the Tertiary period, in many placental and marsupial animals, the part of the brain devoted to the sense of smell decreases in favor of parts of the brain devoted to intelligence. And the forebrain, originally smooth, starts obtaining more and more fissures. Today we know that from one species to another, intelligence and the number of fissures are closely related.

So, it is not surprising that with this double advantage, placental mammals quickly earned an important place among living creatures. Where they had to compete with marsupial mammals, they quickly eliminated many of them. Most of the marsupials today inhabit Australia. Perhaps they even contributed to the downfall of reptiles. In any case, they took over the roles that reptiles had left free.

To appreciate the variety of mammals, let us first go to the calcareous tablelands at Quercy in the South of France, where phosphate used to be mined. And we must go back forty-five million years in time. At the surface of the tableland, there are cracks and pockets hollowed out by water. Deep down, in the caves, there are insects and centipedes. Bats are flying around never hitting the walls, thanks to their built-in radar system. Out in the open, there are mollusks, frogs, snakes, and lizards of the iguana family. A crocodile is lying in wait in the river. But by far the most numerous class are the mammals. The ancestors of ruminants graze in the green fields. In the forest, the graceful lemurs climb in the trees, taking advantage of their freely movable limbs. They are distant ancestors of the modern lemurs from Madagascar. Carnivorous animals are still modeled on their former type. Their paws do not yet have their full strength. Their flesh-eating molars vary in position from one order to another. But in their own way, they already have the physiognomy and mode of life of carnivorous animals today. One resembles a wolf. Another, small, with short legs, is like the skunk. When night falls, another dismembers corpses and crushes their bones like a hyena, with its big grinding teeth. One little, nimble animal has a cat's jaw on a civet's head. A feline with fangs like daggers lies in wait for its victims, splits them open with one blow from its jaws, then feeds on their blood.

In the air, eagles, owls, and secretary birds are flying. All the fauna is that of warm countries and likewise all flora. On the Isle of Wight, in the northern part of the English Channel, among the lakes and on their banks, there are palms, fig trees, catalpas, beeches, and camphor trees. In other places, the forests have oak trees, cypresses, and sequoias, and between the trees there are elegant vines and creepers.

The curtain has now fallen on the warm odors of the Tertiary period. Let us raise it for the last time in the Quaternary period, fifteen or twenty thousand years B.C. France is once again a desert, but this time, a cold desert. A harsh winter covers its plains and mountains with a white cloak of snow. The glaciers, descending from the Alps and Pyrenees, extend as far as Lyon, Grenoble, and Tarbes. In the spring the snow melts and sparse vegetation appears. There is sparse pastureland scattered on the steppes. Willows and dwarf birch trees grow at ground level, and we can perceive some isolated, sparse bushes. Only in the hollows of a few valleys do the fields become thicker. Beautiful ranunculuses and eight-petaled dryads flower. And here grazing are herds of mammoths with their curved tusks and thick coats of hair, woolly rhinoceroses, wild horses, and reindeer. On the tablelands, when autumn comes, the winds blow strongly, spreading dust and sand which become mixed with the freshly fallen snow.

From the edge of a rock, a thin trail of smoke rises. Around a fire, a few rugged people are crouching, covered with animals skins. They look almost like monkeys. But let us follow them back to the darkest room of the cave. On the wall, they have drawn a buffalo. By firelight, they chisel it with a hunting pole, while chanting a solemn song: a prayer that their hunting will be good. Men have arrived in the living world.

And we, who are the distant descendants of these prehistoric men, can today look back at the path that was taken and, thanks to techniques and methods, reconstruct the ancient imagery of life.

From the rapid review that we have just made, we get an impression of beauty and variety, especially variety in the course of time, because the history of life, like that of man, is, according to Jean Piveteau, "the science of phenomena that are not repeated."

But if we try to overcome our admiration and astonishment and judge, if it is possible, only in the light of cold reason, it would be difficult to form many fixed conclusions from what we know today.

We can give an example of our uncertainty. The extinction of species and classes provides us with a very typical one. There are many possible causes of extinction, but at our present state of knowledge, we do not really know which to choose. The main theories that we have outlined lend themselves to criticism. Here is one example. In flowering plants and vertebrates, we thought we could discern a tendency for the new creature's contact with the maternal body to be prolonged more and more in the course of time, and as we reached higher organizational subdivisions. Most fish abandon their eggs. Reptiles prepare holes or nests for them. Birds hatch them, and placental mammals keep them inside their body for a long time, nourishing them, so that they can reach an essential stage of development before being born to lead an independent life. But the same prolonged beneficial contact is already visible in creatures as rudimentary as fresh-water hydra, which are simple sacs with a mouth surrounded by tentacles. Buds form on the maternal body and at her expense, and these become female individuals resembling her in every way. Only then do they become detached to lead a free life. Better still, consider the reproduction of the simplest known organisms, viruses. The bacteriophage, for example, is infinitely closer in space to the bacterial molecules that it remodels after its own structure to make its descendents than the mammalian mother is to the fetus she carries in her womb.

When we try to understand and explain the history of life, we must move with the utmost caution and be wary of many possible illusions. If I gather flowers in a field, it is easy for me to find a small one, a medium sized one, and a large one, and to believe, for example, that the small one comes from the medium one and that the medium sized flower comes from the large one. In reality, this is probably not the case at all. Given a variety of objects, it is always possible to take a certain number of them and classify them in a progressive series, for example, according to whether they get flatter or darker. The series thus established certainly corresponds to the order which we wish to set up in our minds, but does it correspond with reality?

Many analyses of the history of life have been attempted, and marred by basic errors of this kind. A few important facts are taken and the author tries to link them. He always manages to. But every author has a different method. I shall try to extract what is good, and this is considerable, from all of them. But in order to have a broader, more solid foundation, we shall try to follow Descartes' rule: make our enumerations as complete as possible. In this way, we shall be forced to consider frequencies, and even more important, to rely on the firm accuracy of measurements and numbers instead of qualitative impressions that are often vague or illusory. By doing this, we shall comply with the probabilist and quantitative theories of all sciences in general and contemporary biology in particular.

CHAPTER V

✓

The Evolutionary Process

✓

If it is true that plant and animal species are derived one from the other, then they are like a large tree where everything originally stems from the same common trunk. This common trunk then separates into branches, which in turn have boughs, and so on as we move through the series of geological eras, thus approaching our present epoch at the top of the ladder of the ages.

Imagine this tree set in some plastic material. Then, let us cut it into successive horizontal slices. The top slice will represent the present period, and the lower slices will represent older and more ancient periods. The width of the slice will represent a given duration: for example, a minute, a year, a human life, a million years or even more, as we wish. But, the shorter the period, the thinner the slice and the more slices there will be when we cut up the tree. An infinitely small slice (representing a minute or a moment) would show us an instantaneous tableau of life. This tableau, since it is a cross-section of the boughs and twigs, will appear as a series of little round points, rather like in the paintings of the pointillist school. But, since the boughs are separated from each other, the points representing them in our cross-section will also be separated. There will be spaces between them that are filled with the plastic material in which we have set the tree. Thus, at a given moment in the history of life, the species are distinctly separated from each other by clear-cut limits, with no transitional phases. This, too, is the tableau that the present living world shows us. It is only in a few, very rare cases that we find all the transitional forms between two present-day species. As in our

129

tree, set in plastic, it can happen that the slice accidentally passes right through a fork, or a knot.

Now, if we wish to read the course of evolution throughout time from our tree, we should not read from left to right, but from bottom to top, trying to follow one single bough. And immediately this question arises first. Does this bough represent one single species, like a straight line? Or is it composed of successive stumps like a dotted line, where each dot represents a species? Is our tree really a continuous tree, or is it a series of logs or pieces placed end to end?

We ask this latter question independently of the first question. Species that are quite distinct today can be explained both by the continuous development of boughs, each representing one species, or by an interrupted series of pieces placed end to end. The first evolutionists after Lamarck and Darwin, up until 1900, maintained the theory of continuous development, considering the tree really as a tree. Then, after the discovery of abrupt little variations or mutations, in some present-day species, since 1900, many specialists have adopted the theory of a tree composed of separate pieces.

In reality, we must be wary of any preconceived ideas. In our universities, the education of young naturalists is based on the study of present-day plants and animals; that is, it is based on a study of the discontinuous, hence they have a very strong thought pattern acquired in adolescence. By applying this thought pattern to the past, they are tempted to find divisions even if there are none. Moreover, divisions are a necessary or at least an extremely useful device for naming things, classifying them, and labeling them, and for the human mind, they are almost a necessity. Finally, our evidence of the history of life is presented to us by nature in a form that is very conducive to seeing divisions where there are none. Thus, according to reasonable evaluations, about twenty million individuals of a large herbivorous mammal called the anchitherium lived in Southern Germany. Only about seventy of their skeletons have been preserved, and we cannot be sure that these give us an accurate sampling of the species from its beginning to its end. Who knows if all or most of them do not spring from one large epidemic or one large flood in a given year, or even from a series of dry years, like the lean cows of ancient Egypt? These years were only a fleeting instant in the history of the species. No serious statistician would dare to draw any firm conclusions under such uncertain conditions. And even if, in a series of successive layers, we find first one species, then another slightly different species above it with no transition, we know that the areas they occupy could have changed through migrations. Cuvier was the first to recognize this. If the species has emigrated to another place, it could have undergone changes there, due to the effect of different conditions, and then it may have returned to its former habitat in its new form.

In short, our way of thinking, and many of the circumstances, both in the history of life and in the uncertainties of fossilization, tend to make us see more divisions than there actually are in the series of living creatures that have existed throughout the ages.

To get to the bottom of this, we must try to follow series of forms of one and the same genus, and one and the same class, from period to period, or from strata to strata. The best results will be obtained from species represented by the greatest possible number of individuals, in layers that are as continuous as possible, and where the fossil remains have had the most chance of being preserved. The paludinas of Lake Levantin have provided us with a good example, because they show continual variations. There are many other examples too, such as the sea urchins, called *Micraster,* found in the white chalk cliffs at Margate, in the south of England.

From the top of the cliff to the bottom, the chalk, which is ancient marine mud, presents the same whiteness and the same fine grain. This indicates that the conditions of its deposit and the probable chances of preservation are more or less the same. But, close observations of two thousand samples gathered inch by inch, have shown the vertical passing from one species called the *micraster corbovis* to another species, the *micraster coranguinum.* There is a total of five species, as we understand the term, succeeding each other in about five million years. But they follow after each other with imperceptible transitions and no clear-cut limits.

Obviously, the most suitable fauna for this research is that of the very small shell animals living in the sea, such as foraminifera and certain crustaceans. Since they are so tiny, they are very abundant. In one gram of deposit, we can find several hundreds of them. In one layer, one yard thick of the Parisian and North German basins, there are several billions of billions. In comparison with them, the seventy known individuals of the mammal fossil, anchitherium, do not exist. In many limestone and marl deposits, foraminifera and other microscopic organisms are the only fossils found. So they have been the object of very detailed study by oil prospectors. Some of these fossils provide prospectors with valuable information about strata that are otherwise very uniform. But this uniformity is a supplementary proof of success for us, since it probably indicates regular depositing under physical conditions that hardly changed in the course of time.

If we ask the opinion of oil prospectors, we get a reply that is both clear and authoritative: foraminiferan species are usually very varied and difficult to recognize. For the expert, there are few good species, and by this he means species that are easily distinguished from the others, and found only at a given level, a few yards thick, of the cross-section or drilling site. Other species are bad for him, but by that very fact, they are interesting for us.

Mr. Hiltermann, a noted expert, was well aware of this. Let us go to his light, spacious laboratory in Hanover. Men, bent over microscopes, are working. Some are drawing. Others are sorting the countless shells with a very fine needle. In their working hours, they do oil research. But, in their free time, they change jobs. Layer by layer, in the sites that were drilled, Mr. Hiltermann has gathered all the representatives of two genera, from a thickness that represents about six or seven million years. This is a precise and exacting work. Then he counted and measured every batch (several thousands of individuals), using the strictest possible methods in order to discern the possible existence of varieties or breeds.

And the result? Let us take, for example, the genus *Bolivinoides,* a pretty little shellfish with helical whorls like a spiral staircase. Mr. Hiltermann perceived three species of them. In each species, from one layer to the next, we can see variations, but the transitions are imperceptible. In the species *Bolivinoides decorata,* the original form and the final form are very different. The difference is so marked that American specialists, who have a narrower conception of the term "species" than Mr. Hiltermann, would not hesitate to see in them two different species, and even one or two more species for the intermediary forms. But Mr. Hiltermann's statisticians are explicit: all the transitions are there between all these successive forms. In this case, studied by the most modern methods, we can declare that there is continuity between the species, using species in the way that the Americans understand it. And even in the broader sense that Mr. Hiltermann prefers, there is continuity between the *strigillata* species and the *decorata* species. It is only between the *draco* and *decorata* species that Mr. Hiltermann sees a hiatus or a gap and where he is willing to admit an abrupt variation or mutation.

We know that the evolution of a species is favored by geographical isolation. For the foraminifera, evolution must have occurred transitionally in a certain marine basin. Then the new species emigrated to other basins, and, arriving there in its new form, it abruptly supplanted the former species. Mr. Hiltermann's studies of the little animals found at the bottom of the sea at Hanover, eighty or ninety million years old, provide us with a definite example of transition and a possible example of migration. They are only possibly an example of migration, because their appearance could also possibly be explained by abrupt mutation.

Let us go to the most unfavorable case, that of large animals which are relatively scarce and rarely fossilized, like the vertebrates. The progress and discoveries of the past twenty years have revealed the existence of intermediaries. Between reptiles and mammals, intermediaries are found between two hundred million years B.C. and one hundred million years B.C. In animals we still think of as reptiles, the nose and internal ear are already similar to those of mammals. And if the middle ear is still typical of reptiles, this is by definition, because the term reptile implies animals whose middle ear is made like this. If we used the internal ear as our basis for classification, the boundary between the two classes would be elsewhere. Thus, even in the least favorable groups of animals, progress and research tend to reduce the distances between the groups and to illustrate transitions.

In short, in the variations of plant and animal species throughout the ages, fossil remains, when they are numerous enough, give us definite examples of imperceptible transitions. Abrupt divisions in the cycle of mutations are very possible, but not proved. On the tree of life, some boughs at least represent one species. The question of whether other boughs are distinctly separated and cut into stumps is unsettled and not resolved. It is also possible that what seems continuous to us is, in reality, a series of little discontinuous pieces in time. Similarly, in space, the continuity of a beautiful, sandy beach, when viewed through a magnifying glass, becomes broken up into a series of discontinuous grains that form it one by one.

It is paradoxical that when we observe the fossil world, we are exposed to two erroneous conceptions. The discontinuities that are so striking to our eyes probably mask a much greater actual continuity. And the continuities revealed through careful study may mask smaller, fundamental discontinuities.

So, what is the definition of the word species? In the fossil world, there is a lot of uncertainty because there is also uncertainty resulting from the lack of criteria by which we judge lineage. The only logical solution is to consider as different species among the fossils the forms differing from each other as much as the present-day forms differ that resemble them the most. This is the solution instinctively adopted by all the good specialists, as it seemed the most natural. We shall adopt it too, and we use the word species in this sense here whenever we are speaking of extinct forms.

Life expectancy: these promising words have been used by insurance underwriters to designate a deceptive, commonplace notion. If we consider a large group of people of the same age, their life expectancy is the number of years they have left to live if we distribute equally among them the total number of years they all have left to live. This idea implies a certain equality in the face of death or at least in our lives before death. For Frenchmen who are now forty years old, the present life expectancy is about thirty-two years more. At sixty years old, their life expectancy is about sixteen years more. A person's life expectancy at birth is simply the average length of time this person can reasonably expect to live. In the history of plants and animals, it is interesting to speculate on what the life expectancy was for species and genera. When we did not have any means of absolute dating, this was impossible to know. But today, thanks to progress in chronology, it has become possible. This is very interesting for the evolutionist. But life expectancy is important too in the theory of immutability. Even if species did appear independently of each other, they live, in fact, as geology has taught us, for a certain duration, after which they die. They have a life expectancy.

This varies greatly from one species to another. The brevity record seems to be a half million years for some American mammals and for the beautiful ammonites of the Jurassic period. The longevity record is held by certain foraminifera that have been found similar to present species but dating from sixty million years ago, and by a fresh-water crustacean of the Apus genus which has been living for one hundred eighty million years. We are amazed by such longevity. The most transient plant and animal species last five hundred thousand years, one hundred times longer than the history of man. Occasionally, we hear and speak of badly adapted species. But these were able to survive for a very long time all the same. We also see the power of heredity and of the tendency of life to repeat itself; for example, a million successive, identical generations are very common. It is paradoxical that through chronology, modern investigators who support the theory of evolution come to emphasize the extraordinary force of the conservative, immutable tendency of life.

On an average, the life expectancy of animal species is from four to eight million years. Obviously, it is shorter for species that are used as reference marks by geologists in dating strata. For example, the life expectancy of animals of the Cretaceous period and of the elegant graptolites that floated in the waters of the Silurian seas is two million years. It is five or six million years for the fossils used as reference marks in the Devonian and Permian periods; and it is seven million years for the Silurian trilobites. Other fossils, on the other hand, last much longer. The life expectancy of the enigmatic conularia, the mollusks with tentacles of the Silurian period, and several ammonites is twenty million years. It is about thirty million years for some shell fish of the Brachiopoda class.

The plant world forms a similar fan. Some diatoma species, these pretty microscopic algae with lacy carapaces, last a million years. But their life expectancy is seven to eight million years on the average. Plants of the Pliocene period last about two million years. Plants of the Carboniferous period, so different from our plants, last from three to fifty million years, with an average of sixteen million years.

We would expect little unicellular organisms whose generations succeed each other every few days to vary more quickly than the large creatures who reproduce only every few years. But in reality, this is not so. Any difference there may be tends to work the other way. The life expectancy of the tiny diatoma seems to be the same, if not slightly longer, than that of large animals such as horses, carnivorous animals, or elephants. This fact will be useful further on in unraveling the complicated mechanisms of evolution. On an average, the life expectancy of extinct plant and animal species is independent of both the time between generations and geological time. In the phylum of mollusks, the works of different authors who could have had slightly different conceptions of the species give the following successive values from their origin to the present day. Some say three to twelve million years; others say ten million years; and still others say five to seven million years. This means that the average life expectancy in the past four hundred million years has hardly varied. It is a remarkable constant in the history of life. Taking all plants and animals into consideration, the average seems to be between four and eight million years. American scientists have suggested a lower figure—one to three million years—but they have a narrower definition of the term species, and they have devoted more attention to the fossils used as reference marks and having a short life expectancy. This is why we prefer our evaluation of four to eight million years.

The human species to which we belong has existed for several hundred thousand years, which is not very long. We can calculate here our insignificance in the immense duration of life and our chances of continuing to exist.

Plant and animal species are grouped, according to their resemblances, into genera. The genera are grouped in families, the families in orders, the orders in classes, and the classes in phyla. We would expect each of these categories to have a greater life expectancy than the subcategories composing it because these subcategories did not all appear or disappear at the same time and because some could have appeared earlier and others could have disappeared later. And this conjecture has been proved true. Thus, the life expectancies of genera are two to three times greater than those of species. The brevity of life record is from five to six million years for genera, and this is shared by carnivorous animals of the Tertiary period, by horses, and by the very old Cambrian trilobites in Morocco. But, many genera still living today have existed for two hundred forty million years: for example, the sea urchins, called cidaris, with beautiful radial shells. Little shells, similar to the pupa of a fly, belonging to the genus called *pupa,* and living in grass have existed for three hundred fifty million years. The pretty wheel-shaped foraminifera of the genus *rotalia* and the straight foraminifera of the genus *Lagena* have existed close to five hundred million years. The shells on our beaches, the nuculae and the ledas, have existed for more than four hundred sixty million years. But the record is held by the lingulae genus, a Brachiopod shell shaped like a tongue, which is more than five hundred million years old. The average life expectancy for the ammonite genera of the Triassic period is around twenty-five million years and for bivalvular mollusks around seventy million years.

Now let us examine categories that are greater than the genus. The short duration record, for orders, belongs to three orders of mammals which did not survive longer than twenty million years each, in the beginning of the Tertiary era. The average life expectancy for orders today is two hundred thirty million years. For classes, it is about four hundred ninety million years. The gradation obtained, in going from species to genera, then to orders and so on, is very pleasing. For an average sized group, we have found the following values: life expectancy of species, seven million years; of genera, thirty million years; of families, one hundred thirty five million years; of orders, two hundred thirty million years; of classes, four hundred ninety million years. It is certainly very tempting to prolong this progression for even higher categories: for phyla, we have found one billion years; and for kingdoms, around two billion years. The origin of life is situated somewhere between two and five billion years ago.

Thus it is remarkable to have found, by a completely different method, values that are compatible with what we have already estimated as the probable age of the earth, namely from three to four billion years. These values are also compatible with the recent discovery of plants dating from around two billion six hundred million years ago.

There are some risks involved in our estimations. So, after this great leap through time, let us put our feet firmly back on the ground. Even though our method is bold, it does have some good points. And in addition, it confirms the age of life on earth.

Giant dragon fly

But life expectancies do have another interest, which we only thought of while making these surveys for other purposes. On the one hand, we have obtained life expectancies (or precisely: their median values) for *extinct* groups (families, orders, classes, etc.). On the other hand, we have just seen life expectancies that are already fixed, for groups of the same size, but which are still *living*. *A priori,* we could think that these are twice as short. In effect, these groups have already covered a part of their course through life. But if the time had been given them, they would still have another part of their life to live. And if everything happened by chance in the world of groups of living creatures, there would be one chance out of two that the group in question, now living, has already lived at least half of its life. Likewise there is one chance out of two that it hasn't lived half of its life. In other words, if everything happened by chance, the length of life for groups now living would be equal to half the life expectancy of groups that have disappeared.

But it is quite paradoxical that we find very high values that are almost double the others: four hundred ninety million years for classes now living as opposed to two hundred fifty million years for extinct classes; two hundred thirty million years as opposed to one hundred thirty million years for orders; one hundred twenty-five million years as opposed to seventy million years for families.

We can see only one possible explanation. Groups now living and extinct groups with the same size are not equivalent. Living groups are groups that are resistant, lasting, tested, and stable. They have conquered the test of time. Extinct groups represent samples and enterprises that were not successful.

And this brings out one of the fundamental characteristics of the history of life. It has a direction. It is not a series of repetitive cycles. Naturally there are developments, peaks, and downfalls, now of one group, then of another. We shall come to these soon. But these pulsations cannot be equated. There is a movement in life's blood. Tests are made. The least suited are eliminated quite quickly. The best persist, and, as the numbers prove, they have already lasted twice as long.

Let us take a closer look at these competitions.

In 1885, Robert Etheridge, an orderly, conscientious man, was living in London. He was a curator attached to the British Museum and in charge of geology. In this capacity, he classified a countless number of fossils. But "countless" is not really the right word because Robert Etheridge did undertake to count them. Every man has his idiosyncrasies, and Mr. Etheridge had his. He counted the ammonites in England, the trilobites from the Pas-de-Calais, and so on, one by one, and layer by layer. The stamp collector does likewise with his stamps, so does the miser with his securities, and the monarch with his provinces. And what else can one do with a collection other than count it? Mr. Etheridge counted his shells, fossils from the British Isles. And as he was very familiar with them, having studied them for many long years, his inventories were well made. When necessary, he knew how to correct the errors of his predecessors and fill in their gaps.

Let us take a look at Mr. Etheridge's work and examine the largest and best represented group, that of the large and medium marine animals with shells: bivalves, such as mussels, cockles, and oysters; univalvular gastropoda that crawl on one sticky, muscular foot like snails; cephalopoda, such as ammonites and cuttlefish with eight or ten twining tentacles, armed with dreadful suckers like octopuses; two other small groups of mollusks, never numerous; and finally apart from the others, the brachiopoda with two unequal valves and strange, hidden arms. This group of marine animals with shells offers us a lot of advantages. It is the richest in species, thus giving a most extensive foundation for statistics, where the law of large numbers is the most forceful. In 1885, it was one of the best known, and has been studied, occasionally very enthusiastically [1] for more than half a century.

[1] Before Mr. Etheridge, some counts had been made, but almost all of them were broken up, done for one group, then for another group, then for another era. Censuses were very popular with zoologists and botanists from 1850 to 1880. For some (but fortunately not all), this was done in a spirit of self-interest, competition, and with a desire for victory as in a tournament.

"My predecessor found fifty-one species of shells at Dunkirk beach, but I have found one hundred fourteen!" claimed Terquem, a pharmacist and geologist.

This is a dangerous state of mind, because they risk finding more species than there actually are, and counting a simple variety as a distinct species. Errors were committed by some, but not by Mr. Etheridge. But the census method was doomed. The volume devoted to it in the revised edition of

Naturally the number of species found in the British Isles varies according to the eras, first by virtue of the different lengths of these eras. It oscillates between sixty-eight for a short transitional period between the Triassic and Lias periods, and one thousand, two hundred eighty-nine for the longer Lower Jurassic period. Mr. Etheridge has combined them. To make his results comparable, we shall change them to percentages. In other words, from a list of species, classified as bivalves, gastropoda, and so on, we shall calculate by the rule of three how many representatives there are of each group out of one hundred species.[2]

So, we end up with the following picture: successive eras have al-

---

Philip's treatise on geology passed unnoticed by the geologists of the time, whose interest was elsewhere. I found it in the library of a great institute sixty-eight years later, and the pages were not yet cut.

The idea of applying statistics to natural sciences is a very old one. In 1855, an eminent scientist, Baudrimont, addressing an audience of scientists and businessmen from Bordeaux, said: "Gentlemen, no one doubts that from these statistics can emerge laws of the utmost importance for geology and biology or the science of life."

[2] We immediately wonder if the conditions involved were not specific to the British Isles. To verify this, we must make cross checks. They are easy to do. Mr. Etheridge had a predecessor in France. In 1850-1852, Alcide d'Orbigny had published a catalogue of the fossils that were then known, and he had included not only France but all the other countries explored at that time. In reality, d'Orbigny's action was partly useful, but it was also partly unfortunate. A follower of Cuvier, he had pushed the ideas of immutability and catastrophism to extremes. Cuvier had acknowledged four fauna fossils. D'Orbigny distinguished twenty-seven, no more and no less, separated by twenty-six global upheavals. According to him, each of these fauna was derived naturally from a new creation. From one fauna to the next, there was no common species. Or rather, as d'Orbigny was conscientious and because he feared being contradicted, he did admit that a very small number of species, less than one out of a hundred, had been fortunate enough to escape the great cataclysm that had destroyed its fellows. But, according to him, these survivors were the exception. And in other similar cases, he was tempted to give two different names to the same species when it was found at two different levels. He gave in to this temptation.

But if, in d'Orbigny's catalogue, a species is called by one name instead of another, this does not change the group in which he classified it. So, we can treat d'Orbigny's lists like Etheridge's lists. And moreover, except for rare periods, the results are quite similar. So we can conclude that a provisional state of science, even if it was no more advanced than the study of the fossils of the globe in Alcide d'Orbigny's time, can nevertheless offer us a satisfactory basis for certain statistics.

most the same percentages for every group of shells. But eras that are separated have different percentages.

The history of animals with shells, in the sea, throughout the ages, thus shows us three principal periods, separated by two periods of crises. The first period goes from six hundred to three hundred seventy-five million years B.C. Then the brachiopoda were predominant, comprising forty to seventy-five per cent of the species. The other three main groups contain the rest in more or less equal proportions. Around three hundred seventy-five million years B.C., right in the middle of the Devonian period, brachiopoda decrease to about twenty per cent. Bivalvular mollusks then became dominant with around forty per cent of the species. As both these groups have quite similar modes of life, both have two valves, both live immobile on the sea floor, and both live off fine particles of debris and air brought by the water current, we can assume that the replacement of one by the other is the result of competition. This conclusion would have pleased Darwin.

The new balance is maintained with a few ups and downs until around seventy million years B.C. Then, the gastropod mollusks soar up, obtaining an absolute majority of sixty per cent of species. At the same time, two other groups take a sudden fall: cephalopoda and brachiopoda. Both fall to about one per cent. Bivalves remain not far from forty per cent. And these proportions are still found today on the beaches of our oceans and seas.

The flora of the forests and fields, and the coral reefs show us the same sort of variations. But why give further examples? We shall draw our conclusions immediately. In the great drama of life, there are roles to be played on the vacant sets. The same set, and the same theater can be filled many times. The same roles can be played, now by one troupe of actors, now by another. Changes of troupe are often quite abrupt on the scale of geological durations: a few million years. But on the individual scale, the changes are very slow. The brachiopoda empire collapsed without any of its members having time in their short life to know the magnitude of its collapse. Great changes have been relatively few; two to four for every major set during six hundred million years. Life is stable. It does not vary rapidly. From one set to another, changes occasionally occur at the same rate, but not always. Thus a great change occurred around one hundred or one hundred ten million years B.C. in terrestrial plants. Flowering plants and plants with closed ovaries developed, and there was the downfall of large seedless plants. This occurred at a time when shell animals were very balanced and stable in the waves washing up on the neighboring shores.

Instead of following the fate of one role to be played, or one set, we can link up with a troupe and follow its history through the course of time. Here we have much more information because the study of one group of creatures is always more engaging, and easier too, since there are fewer different anatomical types to know. Many groups have been studied in this way.

The variety of groups is enormous. There are marine and terrestrial groups; there are plant and animal groups; and there are microscopic creatures and the giant reptiles and mastodons. The difference in scale here is incomparably greater than between a troupe of puppets and a troupe of actors. And yet, the results show an extraordinary, incredible uniformity. All creatures evolve in the same way in terms of time. From the tiny diatoms, which are plants, to the gigantic dinosaurian animals, there are enormous differences in the way of life. For example, food, movements, and multiplications vary in fantastic proportions. But the duration of the evolutionary phases in time are the same, or of the same order.

On the set of life, the first troupe we shall watch evolving are species of the same genus. In the first phase, lasting from thirty to one hundred million years, with an average of fifty million years, the number of species increases. Using the same metaphor, the newly founded troupe has met with success and the number of actors has grown. But, what is remarkable is that growth occurs at a constant rate, according to the mathematical rule for calculating compound interest. According to the noted Irish scientist Small, in genera of pennal diatoms, the number of species is multiplied by two in seven million years. This means that if there were one species in the beginning, there are two after seven million years, four after fourteen million years, eight after twenty-one million years, sixteen after twenty-eight million years, and so on. The rate varies from one group to another. Thus, in a neighboring group, that of the central diatoms, in the same period of seven million years, the species are multiplied by 1.25 instead of two. So the troupe of central diatoms does not grow as quickly as that of the pennal diatoms. But it does grow at a constant rate, following the same law.

Later, the growth of the troupe of species under consideration slows, as though the troupe were having less success. It goes through a leveling-off stage, then it decreases. Finally, the last actors disappear. The troupe has ended its career, and the genus is extinct. The leveling phase or peak is generally quite short, lasting around ten or twenty million years. Sometimes, as in the sea urchin of the Salenia genus, it forms a real peak. The declining phase varies, but usually it is longer: seventy million years for the Salenia troupe, three hundred twenty million years for the very old lingula troupe, still represented today. A representative of the neighboring genus, the lingulella, was already present in the Pre-Cambrian period. The actors in the family really keep their stand before the footlights.

Sometimes the history of the troupe is marked by crises. Some are specific to one troupe. But the theater of life had a more or less general crisis, two hundred million years ago in the Permian period. At this time, there were three times fewer lingula and four times fewer ancestors of the Latimerian fish than immediately before or immediately after it. We have already had an impression of this crisis in our rapid review of the countryside through the course of time.

The number of genera in the same family, the number of families in the same order, and the number of orders in the same class, varies just like species of the same genus. The main difference is that the total duration is greater. The period of rapid growth is hardly any longer: sixty million years for true ammonite families and also for the spindle-shaped foraminiferan genera; one hundred and ten million years for their rotalid cousins; eighty million years for spiriferid brachiopoda, and as many for the main class of insects and for families in the order of ceratites cephalopoda.

In these large troupes, we find the same peculiarities as in the more modest troupe of species. After the period of rapid growth, there is a peak, as for ceratites cephalopoda families around one hundred ninety million years B.C. Then there is a decline, which is sometimes abrupt, as in the same ceratites, disappearing around one hundred eighty million years B.C. Other times, the decline is very slow, as for the inarticulate brachiopoda, who go from forty-eight around five hundred thirty million years B.C. to forty-three around three hundred seventy-five million years B.C. and seven today. There are also crises at various times, but there is one very constant one, situated about two hundred million years B.C. in the Permian period. At this time, there were only three genera of inarticulate brachiopoda. Also at this time, the gigantostraceans and goniatites cephalopoda became extinct, soon to be replaced by the expanding troupe of ceratites.

In many cases, troupes succeed each other on the same set in an obvious way. For example, in the ocean, the daring cephalopoda, like our squid swimming by propulsion and capturing their prey with the sticky suckers on their tentacles, are represented in the beginning mainly by types of nautiluses, then by goniatites, then by ceratites, and later still by ammonites, and finally, since one hundred sixty-five million years B.C., by cuttlefish, octopuses, and true squid. Likewise, inarticulate brachiopoda were supplanted by the more perfected articulate brachiopoda.

The variations are especially interesting for us right at the beginning and right at the end of the period that we know best: the period extending from six hundred million years ago to the present day. Around six hundred million years B.C., the curve of inarticulate brachiopoda suddenly declines. The only part of the history of this group that we know is their decline, or at least the end of their decline. Judging by the history of all other groups, and in particular the history of articulate brachiopoda, it is obvious that the history of the inarticulata dates back into the Pre-Cambrian era when their expansion and peak period must have occurred. Thus, we can place their origin between seven hundred million and one billion years ago. At the other end of the ladder of time, in our present era, the curves obviously are truncated and stop today. So there are many possibilities open. Some troupes are expanding, as for example the bovine family, or the family of compound flowering plants, or the order of coleopterous insects. Some troupes may be at their peak, like the tiny bryozoan colonies, similar to mosses, that inhabit the sea, or even corals with six major partitions, sea urchins, or gastropod mollusks. Others, finally, are unquestionably declining, for example, reptiles, brachiopoda, dipnoid fish and the Latimeria.

However, there is one difference between troupes of actors and living groups, to which we have closed our eyes until now. Unlike theatrical troupes, living groups grow exclusively by engendering their own new actors themselves. Species have a birth rate. They also have a death rate, limiting the growth of groups, which can lead to their decline and extinction.

We do have an idea of the birth and death rates for groups of fossil species, just as for human populations. We can also derive some information from the isolation experiments conducted naturally since the end of the last glaciation. For example, England separated from the European continent around 5500 B.C. Originally the English stag was of the same breed as stags in France. Fossil remains show us this. Today, it has become slightly different and has formed the Scottish breed with a redder coat. Similar isolations, occurring in North America, in the sea, or in lakes show, too, that in five to twenty thousand years, only subspecies are formed. For species to be formed, more time is needed. And such isolations, linked with the thawing of the great Quaternary glaciers, must have been rare in the history of life, and the formation of species must have been even slower in general. Incidentally, we have noted once again that isolation is one of the greatest causes of the formation of new species. Isolation gives plants, animals, and men originality.

Let us look at the history of the camel family. Their ancestors appeared about 55 million years B.C. in Wyoming and Utah in North America. This was the cradle of these valuable animals. In the beginning, they did not wander far. A strait of water, where Panama now is, stopped them from going down to South America. They could cross neither the North Atlantic nor the Behring Straits. These sturdy animals lived in North America, and there they stayed for forty-five million years. Then about six or ten million years B.C., the isthmus of Panama emerged, and the camel family invaded South America, where they eventually produced llamas, alpacas, and vicuñas. A little later, the family also invaded Asia, probably via Alaska and the Behring region. About five million years B.C., the camel family became established south of the Himalayas. But the ground it had gained on the one hand, it lost on the other. About one million years B.C., at the beginning of the Quaternary era, it disappeared from North America. Since then, it has been found in two separate areas, a South American region and an Asiatic region.

The camel family was very adventurous. During the last million years B.C. (during the Quaternary era), it invaded Siberia, southern Russia, the Near East, and North Africa. Man, by making it a domestic animal, helped in its diffusion, especially in Africa.

The first camel arrived in Paris well before the Romans, probably in pre-Indo-European times, in the era of polished stone, when men did not yet know how to work with metal. Its bones have been found in the silt of the Seine at Saint-Cloud. Among the hundreds of animals found in France, from this era, this is the only one of its species. How did it get there? Spontaneously? This seems impossible. With a caravan led by men. But why? Invaders, merchants or mere travelers?

It is noteworthy that members of the camel family have been domesticated in both the regions they occupy, South America and the Old World, in an almost similar way, as pack animals and for their hair, which is woven into cloth. The natives of South America certainly didn't exchange ideas with the shepherds of the Old World of whom they did not even know. But now and then, in the human race, the same needs and the same degree of psychological and economic evolution produce the same ideas. And the same answer was found in the camel and the wild llama.

With regard to territories thus occupied by species, the Italian scientist Rosa believes that the appearance of a new species is so firmly pre-inscribed in the hereditary patrimony of the mother species that the appearance occurs at the same time in all parts of the territory. This is the hypothesis of hologenesis. "A new species appears possessing world-wide distribution from the very beginning. Species have not enlargened their areas of distribution through migrations. They have not spread from centers; instead they have narrowed their areas of distribution from the whole surface of the globe."

These improbable theories, in contradiction with common sense, always catch our attention. This is what happened with hologenesis. In reality, it is diametrically opposed to a lot of observations. We have seen that isolation is one of the most favorable factors in the differentiation of new species. In addition, nine hundred ninety-nine species out of a thousand are not capable of living in all climates, and therefore of having a world-wide distribution. Finally, if hologenesis were true, in isolated lands like Madagascar, New Zealand, Hawaii, or New Caledonia, we should find as many terrestrial fossil species as on the continents, and these should be the same, since almost the same risks of fossilization were involved. But fewer have been found and they are different. Finally, the example of the camel family is a strong argument against hologenesis, and it is not the only one.

Supporters of hologenesis may have been misled by some attenuating circumstances. Groups easily dispersed, like spore-bearing plants, conquered their territories very quickly—so quickly that our methods for dating the geological past cannot distinguish the beginning and the end of their expansion. Thus, we get the illusion of an enormous, original area. In addition, the period of decline is usually longer and therefore more striking than the period of expansion. Finally, in very ancient eras, less numerous species, as we shall see, generally reached vaster areas than species of today. Jean Piveteau has emphasized the great resemblance between the fish of Greenland and those of Madagascar, some three hundred million years ago, while today, they are very different.

Each time that fossil remains are quite numerous and their dispersion has been slow enough for us to follow the territorial history of a species or higher group, we see the new form originating in a limited area called its cradle, and then extending. Finally, later, and often as a result of the effects of competition, disease, and other mishaps, the area that the species occupies becomes smaller. The species can then become divided or separated. Its last fragments are often inaccessible shelters or refuges, such as distant islands, isolated lakes, and high mountains. The history of the kangaroo and its family, the marsupials, is a good example. Formerly, forty-five million years ago, they were found in Montmartre. It is there that Cuvier found their skeletons. They were also found in Europe, Africa, Asia, and in North and South America. Then, in the northern hemisphere, they had to compete with the more robust, hardy, placental mammals, better conditioned for raising their young. So marsupials disappeared from all of the Old World, and are found in only two southern refuges; Australia and South America, with a rear guard in the United States.

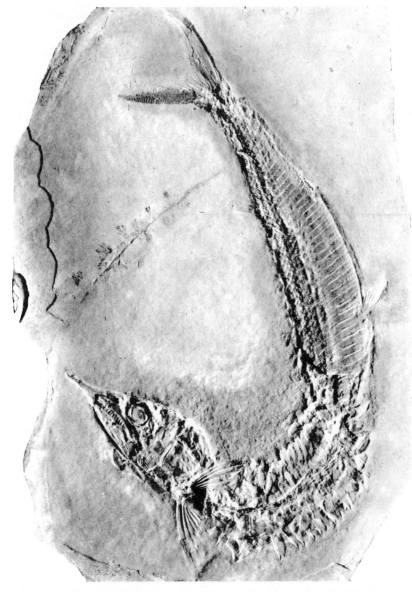

Imprint of the death throes of a fish inscribed in mud: this fish, found at Solenhofen in Bavaria, is one hundred fifteen million years old.

How are these cradles and refuges distributed in the vast world? To know this, we must consult a statistical inventory, and in fact, one geologist, Mrs. Bouillet made one. She collected together all the data on one hundred and sixty terrestrial or fresh water fossil groups, and she transferred it onto planispheres. The distribution of the cradles of species was shown to be very simple. It is almost proportional to the respective surface areas of the continents and other lands studied. It seems as though new groups used to appear here and there by chance, like buttercups or daisies flowering in a meadow in the springtime.

The table is quite different for the shelters and last refuges of species, before their extinction. Islands have the most groups: New Zealand, Madagascar, and Indonesia. Then come very isolated lands: Australia and South America. On the other hand, we find very few refuges in Africa and North America, and even less in the European and Asian continents, which are vast, single stretches of land. It is clear that the more isolated and distant a land is, the longer new families, born elsewhere, take to get there, and the longer ancient families, sheltered from competition, can persist there too.

CHAPTER   VI

◆

Evolutionary Tendencies

◆

Is the course of evolution directed by free will toward a goal? Or is it imposed by an implacable and blind physical force that is an inherent property of all matter? These are the questions man must consider every time he discerns or thinks he discerns a movement in a certain direction in nature.

Does the history of life show us such a movement? To know this, we must first consider the forms and then the number of species. Working in this way, we will more or less follow historical order. The supporters of evolution who came after Darwin attached a lot of importance to series of fossils ordered in a regular gradation in successive eras. We have already mentioned the examples of large groups of vertebrates and terrestrial plants and the ancestors of the horse.

The evolution of the horse family, for about sixty million years, did not occur following one single line; it branched into several. These are branches off a main trunk. While the main trunk was evolving in America, three branches emigrated to Europe around fifty, twenty-five, and ten million years B.C. respectively. Two other main branches became separated first in America. One went to South America around two million years B.C. At times there have been up to eight contemporary progenies in America. The size of the animal grew in the main trunk, but it decreased slightly in some branches. The transition from a foot with three toes to a foot with one toe, characteristic of the horse today, was not gradual but quite abrupt. Evolutionary speeds varied.

Consider again the ancestors of the camel and llama. Between sixty-five and thirty-five million years B.C., their size changed from that of a large hare to that of a gazelle. Around fifteen million years B.C., it was somewhere between a llama and a camel. Sixty million years B.C., they had four hooves, four digits, and four bones in the forefoot. Thirty-five million years B.C., they had only two. In the llama today, the two bones of the forefoot are soldered together as in oxen or sheep.

Look at the craniums of future elephants. Originally, fifty-five million years ago, elephants tended to resemble bears. They had no trunk and no tusks. Then from era to era, up until the present day, they grew larger in size, their noses lengthened into trunks, the two nostrils of which can still be seen at the end. And at the same time, their incisors lengthened into tusks.

About sixty-five million years B.C., running through the fields of North America, there was a gracious animal the size of a fox, but not as voracious. It was a herbivorous animal. It had only one dominant digit, like the horse or tapir. Did this little animal suspect its fate? The family was then in the prime of its youth. But twenty million years were sufficient for it to make its way gradually to the gigantic size of the titanothere and its mongolian relations. It became titanic in size, with a squat body and low head. Its snout was thick, and it had ridiculously small eyes. Low on its forehead, there were two terrible growths, which gradually moved down toward its nose, from era to era, becoming two horns, and finally being linked together as one. However, its feet and toes did not change, unlike the horse. This is one of the essential characteristics in the history of life from one group to another. There are differences in the speed at which evolution occurs. An organ evolving quickly in this animal evolves more slowly in that animal.

The main groups themselves appear, in geological eras, following an order of progressive complication. We saw this for vertebrates and flowering plants. It is a general fact. Let us take the largest phylum, that of articulata. The peripati, tiny little creatures, like worms with legs, have existed since five hundred thirty million years B.C.; the first centipedes since four hundred fifty million years B.C.; the first dwarf, wingless insects, since three hundred seventy-five million years B.C. Winged insects have been found only since about three hundred fifty million years B.C.; of them, metamorphic insects only appeared around three hundred million years B.C. Thus the articulata have appeared in the very order that indicates their anatomical progress.

In short, in the large groups and even in the small groups, in spite of detours, reversals, or deviations, evolution does not occur purely by chance in any direction. It has dominant lines, or orthogeneses, as the experts say, which is evolution in a straight line.

Now, we must ask ourselves where they lead.

At this point, we are threatened by perils, which this comparison may help us to understand.

Here we are on a Saturday morning at the Saint-Cheron station less than one hour from Paris. There are passengers on the platform about to leave.

One of the passengers, a young man, tells us, "Residents of Saint-Cheron have to go to Paris to work."

But an old woman points to the opposite platform where there are two women with baskets on their arms, going in the opposite direction.

"People from this town go to Dourdan: it's market day today."

Paris or Dourdan? Is there a dominant direction of traffic from Saint-Cheron? There is a very simple way of finding out: by asking the station master. He will then explain to us that he sells four times more tickets to Paris than to Dourdan. Paris is the rule; Dourdan, the exception. But without this information from the station master, if we had to rely on vague impressions, we could have made three mistakes:

(1) See only the rule, generalize excessively, and declare, "The traffic from Saint-Cheron moves toward Paris."

(2) See only the exception and be taken in by the paradox, "Contrary to appearances, it is the little nearby town that attracts more people than the great city further away. The traffic from Saint-Cheron moves toward Dourdan."

(3) Or finally, with apparent wisdom, accept as correct the statements of both the young man and the old woman. This is putting the

exception on the same footing as the rule and declaring, "There is as much traffic toward Paris as there is toward Dourdan. There is no dominant direction."

Similarly, in the history of plants and animals, there are both rules and exceptions in most domains. The problem is one of their relative frequencies, and these we must learn to evaluate correctly. Our impressions and our judgment can contribute in this, on condition that we are cautious. It is better to rely on measurements and counts wherever possible. Let us start with the size of individuals.

In a large number of groups, in the course of time, the size has increased. The horse, camel, elephant, and titanothere families have given us good examples. At the other end of the scale of creatures, unicellular organisms provide us with other examples. Orbitolines, round and flat like coins, are only a few millimeters large in the Cretaceous period. Ten million years later, they have grown to thirty millimeters, the size of a five franc coin. In the mountains at La Clape and Corbieres, we can see all the transitions between the medium sized forms, just as in the paludinas of Lake Levantin.

Naturally there are exceptions. Thus, during the Quaternary era, geologically quite recent, there were dwarf elephants, no bigger than ponies, living not far from the big elephants. The skeletons of these strange animals, perfectly ossified and therefore adult animals, are found mainly in the Mediterranean islands of Malta, Sicily, Cyprus, and Sardinia, and in peninsulas in Greece, near Rome, and on Gibraltar. So, we can rightly see the effects of isolation. But such cases, as strange and noteworthy as they are, are nevertheless exceptions, just as the people traveling to Dourdan do not stop the people traveling to Paris from being more numerous.

Increase in size is such a fundamental tendency that, during the ages, it is continuous in one and the same type of form and way of life. It can be seen in groups which, in spite of their differences, are linked by the common role they play. Invertebrate animals living in the water reached four centimeters in the pre-Cambrian period, with the lingulella, a tongue-shaped brachiopod. Six hundred million years ago, the record was held by a jellyfish that was eighteen centimeters. Around five hundred thirty million years B.C., this record was broken by a short-headed trilobite measuring nineteen centimeters. Around four hundred fifty million years B.C., tubular mollusks with tentacles and a straight shell reached a size of six feet, and around three hundred eighty million years B.C., the gigantostracean articulata broke this record by measuring ten feet. Now, in our present era, some deep sea squid measure fifty-eight feet with their arms outstretched.

Still in the sea, vertebrates show a similar gradation. Around four hundred fifty million years B.C., an armor-plated fish measured fourteen centimeters. Around three hundred ninety million years B.C., another reached twenty-five centimeters. Around three hundred seventy million years B.C., one of the shark's ancestors measured almost six feet. Around three hundred twenty million years B.C., an amphibian from a developing group broke this record by measuring ten feet. But the marine reptiles broke all records. About one hundred seventy million years B.C., an ichthyosaur measured over thirty feet. About eighty million years B.C., the mosasaur from Maestricht measured thirty-nine feet and the elasmosaur forty-nine feet. Then the reptiles became extinct, but when the new order of placental mammals developed, they took the record and have kept it to this day, with the whale measuring from fifty to sixty feet and the rorqual measuring up to 100 feet.

On the land, in the open air, the same progression can be seen in plants and animals. It would be exhausting to list all the examples. So let us look at the aerial parts of plants. About four hundred fifty million years B.C., in Australia, they do not exceed more than a few decimeters. About three hundred ninety million years B.C., a spore-bearing plant measured ten feet. Around three hundred fifty-five million years B.C., a tree sixteen feet high was found. About three hundred twenty million years B.C., there were beautiful trees one hundred feet high. Finally, today, seed plants such as the lofty sequoia trees reach three hundred and twenty-five feet, and eucalyptus trees with their light foliage are up to three hundred feet high.

Throughout time, there are highs and lows, just as in sports, where world records are not broken every day. Thus the record wingspread in flying creatures was twenty-eight inches in a type of dragonfly around three hundred twenty million years B.C. Then it was lower. Around one hundred eighty million years B.C., the first flying reptiles were no bigger than sparrows. But, about one hundred seventy-five million years B.C., they broke the record, with a wingspread of more than six feet. Around eighty million years B.C., they have a wingspread of twenty-six feet. Then they disappear. The birds succeeding them are well below this. Today, even the eagle has a wingspread of only ten feet. Obviously evolution is not in a straight line here. But this exception does not detract in any way from its value as a rule. As a general rule, in the course of time, plants and animals have tended to become larger and larger.

We have wondered if it is advantageous for plants and animals to grow in this way, and if so, what is the advantage? For terrestrial plants, this is clear. The thickness of the atmosphere with which they are in contact increases with their height, and accordingly so do the exchange surfaces through which they take their carbon from the air. To keep to averages, their vital space in height thus passes from eight to twelve inches around four hundred fifty million years B.C. to sixty-five to one hundred feet in our forests today. And the whole world of forest plants and animals participates in this expansion.

Animals have several advantages in being large. One of these was discovered or confirmed quite accidentally during research undertaken by the Minister of Agriculture for Great Britain in 1940. Because of the war, there was a shortage of food. Among other things, horses' food was studied. It was then seen that their diet consisted of two parts. One, assuring their very maintenance, was proportional to their surface area, that is, proportional to the square of their length. The other part, covering the mechanical work done by the animal, was proportional to its weight, that is to the cube of its length. So it was seen in horses that the longer the horse, the more important the second part became in relation to the first. On equal rations, a large horse will perform more work than two small horses. The bigger the animal, the more efficient it is.

A second advantage was pointed out by a very wise scientist, Mathias Matschinski. Judging by nature today, the larger the size, the greater the speed. And with increased speed, there is an increase in the opportunities to attack, flee, move out in search of new pastures, or to pursue prey. In aquatic creatures between one-tenth of a millimeter and one meter, that is, over an enormous scale of dimensions, speed is more or less proportional to size. Even here odd relays are established. Organisms measuring a few hundredths of a millimeter swim by undulating a tail: for example, oval unicellular organisms, animals or algae. At a few tenths of a millimeter, greater speed is attained by ciliated organisms called infusorians. Beyond these, measuring about one centimeter, we have crustaceans that propel themselves with a type of paddle. Swimming by undulations gains the ascendancy with fish, dolphins, and whales. A Russian scientist, Chouleikine, has shown in a statistical study that at every dimensional stage, the swimming mechanism adopted is the one giving the greatest speeds. So the adaptation of swimming animals is excellent.

But it does have limits. The speed hardly increases from the dolphin to the whale. It reaches a ceiling between fifty and sixty-five feet per second. Perhaps this is one of the reasons that there are not larger creatures in the water. They would have no advantage, and no doubt natural selection would eliminate them. Another reason, or perhaps the same presented differently, is that the effort necessary to move an animal is proportional to its weight, that is, to the cube of its length, while the effort spent is proportional to the section of its muscles, that is, to only the square of the length. Food exchanges, absorption, and respiration, which provide the energy necessary for the work, also vary in similar animals, like the square of the length. When the length increases but the form remains the same, there comes a time when the work possible is inferior to the work needed, and so organisms that are too big are at a disadvantage. It is sufficient to have seen a bullfight where the man, by his agility, can dodge the bull's charge, bearing straight ahead by the forces of inertia, to be able to understand that beyond a certain limit, mass is no longer an advantage. In some large animals, it is remedied by various prolongations, like the elephant's trunk. Similarly, the strange, long, slender, and supple neck of the diplodocus could reach into the tall grass to graze, and thus it avoided having to displace its enormous body.

As the size of the adult was increasing, so was the average length of life of creatures, judging by nature today. No doubt for equal sizes there is a wide margin of variations. A man lives three times longer than a donkey or a sheep. But all these fluctuations are details that should not mask an impressive over-all correlation. A bacterium measures one thousandth of a millimeter and lives for a half hour. Infusorians, one hundred times larger, live six to ten hours. An insect measuring a centimeter lives for one year; a cat, fifteen years; an elephant, seventy years; a sequoia tree three hundred feet high can live for more than two thousand years. During the ages, since living creatures have been increasing their size, their life span has probably been increasing too.

Judging by the living species of today, length of life is roughly proportional to size, that is, to the relationship between the animal's volume and its surface area. Moreover, the food consumed and assimilated by a plant or animal is roughly proportional to its surface area. Thus, we have calculated that during its life, an organism (other than a virus) renews its own matter about two hundred times. And this proportion has not varied much in the course of the ages.

At the same time as they were tending to become larger on the whole, living creatures were also becoming more complex. Giraud-Soulavie noted this in 1780, with his usual lucidity. Both tendencies are distinct. An ox is not more complex than a sheep, nor is an oak more complex than a daisy. But as a rule, a larger size offers greater possibilities for more intricate structures in the diversity of living creatures. In an organism measuring one tenth of a millimeter, an infusorian for example, there is no room for a heart or for a respiratory apparatus. Moreover, the animal would derive no benefit from them. Thanks to its small size, it can breathe directly through the wall of its only cell, and the internal movements of its basic mass are sufficient to mix and carry the food and oxygen to all parts of its body and to drain the carbon dioxide and other waste products. Thus the organism does not need a heart, veins, or arteries. These mechanisms are not as simple as this short review would lead us to believe; but in larger organisms, for example the shrimp, these same detailed functions are relegated to specialized cells in organs, and in addition, there are other organs of the creature which have become necessary because of its very size. A shrimp could not survive without a digestive tube, fish-gills to breathe, a heart which makes its blood circulate, and vessels which carry the blood to even the smallest organs and bring it back. The shrimp species would be extinct if it did not have genital glands and organs permitting it to reproduce.

Plant and animal fossils show us many examples of progressive complication. In the *Jamoytius,* which is the most distant ancestor of vertebrates, the mouth, as we have seen, is a simple opening, with no jaws, unable to chew or bite. Behind the opening, there is a pharynx, with rows of slits on each side supporting rigid arched pieces. The animal takes in water through its mouth and expels it through its slits, where respiratory exchanges occur. The fine particles in suspension are taken to the stomach, then to the intestine. This was the situation about four hundred fifty million years B.C. But already, at that time, the first respiratory arch was missing and the second arch from the front was replaced by a bottom jaw. Now the mouth can grasp food. The other arches remain unchanged and are still used in breathing.

Around three hundred ninety million years B.C., in other fish, the third arch has now become attached to the lower jaw, and it helps this jaw to articulate with the cranium. Almost at the same time, in amphibians, the remaining arches lose their respiratory function in the adult, and the slits disappear. But their third arch remains free and available to a certain extent. An innovation appears in reptiles around three hundred twenty million years B.C. An extension of the throat, like the finger of a glove insinuates itself between the internal ear and the skin. The cavity of the middle ear is formed and the available third arch forms the skeleton of it by becoming an ossicle. Finally, around one hundred eighty million years B.C., after a whole series of transitions, mammals now have three ossicles called the hammer, anvil, and stirrup depending on the third arch. And in the middle ear, they transmit vibrations from the eardrum to the internal ear. The external ear has also appeared. Its role is to receive and concentrate the sounds. Creatures have become complex, and the complexities obviously have their uses.

These uses are also evident in the evolution of the cerebrum of vertebrates. Their cerebrum is still very simple around four hundred fifty million years B.C., but it gradually gets perfected and reaches its greatest degree of development now with man.

The noted biologist Julian Huxley, grandson of Darwin's gallant companion, has invited us to review the progressive development of the animal kingdom from the simplest organism to the most complex. What were the most striking stages? Starting from the unicellular organism, Julian Huxley has suggested four. The first important step is the grouping of several cells, for example the organization of animals into sac-like structures, like fresh water hydra of today. The second step is the appearance of a differentiated head, as in worms and crustaceans. The third step is the appearance of a lung or trachea allowing the creature to breathe in the open air. Finally, the fourth step is the ability of warm-blooded animals to maintain a constant temperature. This is found only in birds and mammals, and it assures the internal environment, where the cells live, a very great independence in relation to the external environment, which is exposed to great temperature variations. If we now try to situate these steps in time and in the chronology of the history of life, then we see that the first two steps, namely multicellular organisms and organisms with a head, were accomplished before five hundred eighty million years B.C. At this time, there were already animals with a head, and some, such as trilobites, had a very pronounced head. Lungs appear around three hundred ninety million years B.C., and warm-blooded animals possibly between one hundred eighty and two hundred fifty million years B.C. These stages and dates can be projected onto a graph. It is obviously very risky to extend the part of the curve we do know into the distant past. But if we do take the risk, we find unicellular organisms originating between three and four billion years ago. Once again, these values coincide with what we have estimated elsewhere for the age of the earth (about three to four billion years) and the age of life.

The plant world offers us very similar examples. Still sticking to an over-all view, this time we shall follow the German botanist, Zimmermann. Above all, Zimmermann is an expert with the microscope. He has studied very enlarged cross-sections of plant fossils. Naturally he sees the cells in these. And as there is nothing else to see, he has examined them very carefully, noting their differences and classifying them into different types. He works conscientiously and meticulously, perhaps too much so, because he has really distinguished too many types of cells. He has found up to seventy-six in the same plant, and this is probably exaggerated. But for us this is unimportant, because the essential is that Zimmermann has observed the fossil remains of all ages equally carefully. So his results can be compared. In the plants of five hundred eighty million years ago, he distinguishes seven types of cells in the same individual; four hundred ninety million years ago, eleven types of cells; three hundred sixty million years ago, twenty-six types of cells; two hundred thirty million years ago, forty-eight types of cells; one hundred twenty million years ago, sixty-two types; and sixty million years ago, seventy-six types of cells.

Thus even the most detailed anatomy of plants, even the very cells making up their bodies, have become more complex in the course of time. And we can go even further than Zimmermann and make a graph of the number of cells in terms of the dates quoted above. We note that the number of cells has grown very regularly, following a geometric progression. It has doubled approximately every one hundred forty million years, between five hundred million years B.C. and our present era. This result is even more remarkable since Zimmermann did not have the slightest idea of the mathematical law that his data would follow when he patiently set about studying and counting. He did not even try to establish it, and he obviously did not know that one day we would be able to use his patient and praiseworthy work in this way.

There is one difficulty that we should mention in all honesty. If we do extend the law into a more distant past, we obtain a date of nine hundred million or one billion years B.C. for the era when plants had only one type of cell. But algae and fungi have already been found dating from two billion, six hundred million years B.C., and it is possible that they already had several types of cells. If this is true, and if Zimmermann's values are accurate, we must conclude that the time they took to divide into two was longer in the distant past than in the near past. In other words, recent acceleration has been more rapid than indicated by the geometric progression.

We shall take a step forward if we now try to find out where this distinct progressive complexity that we have discerned leads. What is its purpose and how do plants and animals benefit by it? So we must consider its usefulness. Its uselessness will be shown later.

Often the oldest representative of a group, because of its constitution, is able to lead ways of life that are more varied than many of its successors. The oldest carnivorous mammals, for example, had jaws not too dissimilar from those of the bear, which in nature today can choose between eating fish, meat, berries, or honey. On the other hand, the lion or tiger, both more recent animals, are specialized in eating herbivorous animals. The fox is specialized in eating birds, the ferret in eating rabbits, which he pursues into their burrows thanks to his slender body and short legs. We could quote many other examples of such specialization, like the horse, whose long legs make it ideal for racing and whose neck is ideal for grazing and whose molars are ideal for grinding the grass.

As an argument against this idea of specialization, some naturalists reply that in many instances specializations have existed from the very beginning. But supporters of the idea of specialization point out that after a group has become specialized, it does not go back to a nonspecialized form.

Their opponents concede this essential point to them. But they have counterattacked by pointing out that there are other groups which are no less important that are not very specialized—such as the brachiopod lingula for example. Or their specialization is not obvious. In what way were the plants of one hundred and fifty million years ago less specialized than ours? There were already trees, grasses, marsh plants, and other plants growing in dry areas. No doubt, since then, the embryo has become more protected. It has become more complex, but is this specialization?

The pictures of past life, when we look at them, do suggest a step forward. The first living organisms lived in water, in the sea, in rivers, and in lakes. Their remains are quite numerous between five hundred eighty and four hundred fifty million years B.C., in case anyone should doubt this. At the very most, a few plants were scattering their reproductive particles into the open air. Then plants and animals gradually settled down on the land, first on the bottom of dry swamps, later on land that had never been covered with water. We have followed these steps. The conquest began around five hundred eighty million years B.C. And it was certainly completed by one hundred eighty million years B.C. and possibly even before. A duration of four hundred million years is very short if we compare it to the three billion years of previous life that was wholly marine life.

Immediately after the land, the air became colonized. The first flying creatures, which were insects, date from three hundred forty million years B.C. Plants conquered the air in their own way, by erecting their stems and branches. This subdivided the aerial space and offered ready-made landing sites for insects, then other flying animals. And it offered resting places for mosses and lichens and for all flora and fauna that lived off them and on them.

It is quite clear that all these ways of life, terrestrial or aerial, and all these places to be filled and the roles to be played, in fact all these specializations, were innovations in the history of life. The roles, such as manufacturers of organic matter, consumers, herbivorous or carnivorous animals, burrowing or climbing animals, running, crawling, or flying animals, all these specializations are innovations acquired since around four hundred fifty million years B.C. They did not exist during the long billions of years of previous aquatic life. They are a recent conquest.

Thanks to fossils, we can kill two birds with one stone. We can discern in life a tendency to conquer and a tendency toward territorial expansion. And there is a striking confirmation of life's general tendency to become diversified and specialized.

But all voices and all opinions should be heard. So once again, we are in the position of the inquirer on the platform of the Saint-Cheron railway station. Among thinkers, some still shake their heads and say: "Life continually makes and remakes creatures and things. Like history, it is a perpetual new start." Others declare: "No, life never moves backward. If it starts afresh, it is never in exactly the same way." Life goes forward. Edgar Quinet, in 1870, expressed this thought: "Nature does not turn back. It does not remake what it has destroyed. It does not recast the mold that it has broken. In the infinite number of combinations locked in the future, you never see the same humanity twice, nor the same flora, nor the same fauna."

What do fossils tell us about this? Naturalists point out numerous cases where a species seems to have moved backward, in certain respects, with regard to a certain organ or a certain function. Or it seems to have moved against the general main tendencies that we have discerned. For example, it seems that dwarf elephant fossils from the Mediterranean islands (the fossil from Cyprus does not even measure three feet) are descendants of the large species which is the ancient elephant. This ancient elephant has been found fossilized throughout France. This is just the opposite of the law of increased size.

In the oldest mollusks with tentacular arms, the partitions subdividing the shell form lines that are barely sinuous when they meet the shell wall. Later, in ammonites, the contact sutures form complicated, strange patterns. But in the quite recent genera of neolobites, these sutures are as simple as in their ancestors. In this anatomical detail, there is obviously an exception to the law of progressive complication, and we see a return to an older state. On the other hand, all the other features of neolobites are recent types.

Let us look at the ancestors of the whale from very ancient times, around four hundred million years B.C. They are fish. They swim in the water, and they breathe through slits on the sides of their necks. Then, through the ages, they have come to live in the open air. They have become amphibians, reptiles, then mammals. They have acquired pairs of legs on the plan of our limbs, lungs, and a constant temperature. They have lost their respiratory slits, first in the adult, then in the young animal, where only the trace of them can be found today in the form of folds in the fetus. The teeth have become differentiated into incisors, canines, and molars. The female animal has acquired nipples and the male an organ for copulation.

And then, sometime between seventy and twenty-five million years B.C., the situation becomes reversed for the whale. The terrestrial creature becomes a marine creature again. How? Does it go back over the same ground but in the opposite direction? Does it become a fish again? Does it lose its lungs, its constant temperature, and its nipples? Do its respiratory slits come back? Not at all, it stays a mammal. From the fish, it recovers only the indispensable mechanisms necessary to survive. It takes back its tapered form again and can swim rapidly by undulating, but it still retains a mammalian skeleton and mammalian muscles. The whale's flesh is red. It tastes like meat, but is rather bland. Two fins, on the right and left, maintain its balance, but they are on the plan of the limbs of quadrupeds. The whale rediscovers the simple food of its very ancient ancestor, Jamoytius. It feeds on little microscopic organisms floating in the water. But it captures them quite differently, by means of frayed, horny plates along each side of its upper jaw. These are horny like the nails and the hair of other mammals.

Yes, if we look closely, evolution is irreversible. Edgar Quinet was right. Nature never moves backward. In the immense number of known filiations of extinct plants and animals and of living plants and animals, we do not know of one single case where there is an exact return to a form that has disappeared. We can explain why in this way. The ancient creature living four or five million years ago was adapted to a certain physical environment and to a certain circle of animals and plants living in its era. They were its friends, enemies, indifferent creatures, or prey. They lived in equilibrium with each other. But since then, the physical world has changed slightly, and the living world has changed a lot. All present species are newcomers and are very different, and it would really be a miracle for the ancient creature who is adapted to its ancient surroundings still to be adapted to these new surroundings. Could a Gallic man returning to French society in the atomic age feel at ease amidst the din of airplanes and automobiles?

Let us return once again to our friend the whale. Its immediate ancestors are terrestrial mammals who obviously had four legs. But the whale has only two limbs, and these are forelimbs. Its rear limbs have disappeared, or at least they are not evident in the fetus. In the adult whale, they are only two tiny stilettos, drowned in flesh. They are a good example of rudimentary organs, an obvious simplification and a new exception to the law of complication. Similar regressions occur frequently, as for example the side digits of the horse and the camel, the tail of birds and many monkeys. But it is always a question of a very limited number of organs. Many other organs in the same creatures have evolved progressively, such as the wings of birds, the forepaws of monkeys, and the horny plates of the whale. Then, this question comes to mind. Why, in the same creature, do some organs progress while others regress? Fossil series all give us the same answer. Organs that evolve are serviceable organs. Organs that regress are those that have no use. A century and a half of patient research has brought us to this point, suggested by Lamarck. We shall discuss the mechanisms producing this evolution further on. The important point is to be aware of this fact.

Decreases in size, simplifications, regression, and backward movements are occasionally observed in the history of life. However, they are relatively rare exceptions to these general rules that still stand: namely, the evolution toward greater size and complexity, the abandonment of what is not useful, the development of what is useful, specialization, expansion, and conquest.

When we go to the movies, there is only one film being shown at a time, on one screen. Theater managers have not yet thought of showing two films at the same time on two adjacent screens. But naturalists have used this idea in their own domain. It is an amusing idea that allows us to make comparisons between two different evolutions. In addition, it poses some interesting problems: namely the problems of convergence and parallelism, with all their intermediary stages. If there is parallelism, the two films will be very similar. They will start with similar situations and end with the same ending. If there is convergence, the films will not be similar to start with. They will begin with different situations, but they will have the same ending all the same.

Convergence, for example, can be seen in the same type of head among vertebrates living in water but breathing in air, with their nostrils and eyes out of the water. This type of head is seen in the hippopotamus, the crocodile, and also the frog, yet they have very different immediate ancestors.

Another example of convergence can be seen in the past history of the toothless, winged reptiles and the past history of birds. The winged reptile has light, hollow bones like birds. The beak is horny, and its head makes the characteristic right angle with its long, strong neck. It really is like a bird. And yet, the rest of its anatomy classifies it as a reptile, and its immediate ancestors are reptiles.

Convergence can be found in the structure of the wing which has appeared in four groups in the course of time, and in each group, it has appeared by different means. In the bird, the wing has the whole arm as a frame. In the reptile, it has only one excessively long digit. In the bat, it has five, very long, separated digits. In insects, it has the tracheae, which are ramifications of the respiratory apparatus. In passing, we should note that this represents a new argument against the theory of immutability. If immutability were true, and if the function were the goal of the organ, not its effectiveness, we

CONVERGENCES

They come from different families and yet there is a great resemblance due to the same way of life. Note the noses and eyes in the air.

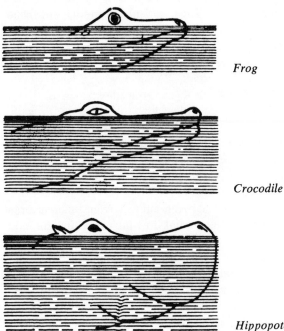

Frog

Crocodile

Hippopotamus

could possibly expect one single type of organization for every function and not several, as is the case here.

Another example of convergence can be found in the beautiful slender forms gliding through the water with fins on their backs, as seen in the whale, the shark, and the ichthyosaur.

Now let us go to the jungles of India to observe the giant panda. It belongs to the same order as bears and civet cats. But instead of eating flesh like other self-respecting carnivorous animals, it feeds on plants and bamboo shoots. It grasps the stems like a man, with its large hand open. Let us take a closer look. What appears to be a thumb is not really one; it is an extension of the wrist, supported by a bone, and it works in opposition to the other digits. The real thumb is one of these other digits, but it has stayed in line next to the index. Like the monkey's hand, the panda's hand can grasp, but it has evolved quite differently from the monkey's hand. And the panda has completely different ancestors, namely bears and dogs.

Convergence can also be seen on a microscopic scale and between very distant groups. Thus, articulata on the one hand and vertebrates on the other, although they belong to two different phyla, both have striated muscles with alternating clear disks and dark disks. Their most noteworthy property is in allowing more rapid movement than smooth muscles. Watch a wasp's wing vibrating in the sunlight and you will see their extraordinary speed.

The tracheae, which are little white tubes full of air with spiracles or external openings controlling the passage of air, exist in insects and in certain spiders. But these two classes of articulata belong to two very different superclasses, since insects are similar to crustaceans and spiders to limuli. So this is a transition between convergence and parallelism.

Parallelism can be seen between animals from different branches, but stemming from a common trunk to which they are still close, for example the different sub-orders or families of hooved mammals. The ancestors of the rhinoceros, the camel, the bull, and others, all show the same evolutionary tendencies that we have seen in the horse. Their size increases, the number of digits decreases, the number of bones in the palm and the ball of the foot both decrease, and their limbs get longer. They have molars, and the enamel on their crowns becomes more accentuated. Their necks get longer and more powerful. The animal is better adapted to graze and to run. If oxen appear heavy to us, we must not forget the effects of their domestication. Think of herds of bisons disappearing in a cloud of dust or the frenzied bull's charge at a bullfight.

Parallelism can also be found in the placid amphibians. Originally their cranium was arched and well-ossified, and the palatine bone was almost continuous. Then in three ancient fossil orders, parallel evolution occurs in the same direction and finally results in a flat cranium that is barely ossified. The palatine becomes fenestrated, as can be seen today in frogs and salamanders.

The facts are so clear that no one thinks of refuting them. But when it comes to understanding them, we have several opinions from which to choose. With convergence in mind, consider the wings of birds, winged reptiles, bats, and insects, even though they are made on different plans. All are well-adapted to the same, very characteristic function of flying. Convergence only illustrates in a very expressive way the problem of adaptation. We have already spoken of adaptation in passing. And we shall return to it later.

But wings are adapted not only to their function but also to the environment where they exercise this function. Directly or indirectly, the external environment has played a role in this adaptation and in convergence in particular.

With parallelism, we are tempted to think of some internal force or cause within the living creatures themselves. This would be a force that they share with their fellows and which they have inherited from their common ancestors, to whom they are still close. Of the three types of amphibian fossils showing us the same parallel evolution of the head, two used to live in fresh water, and the third lived on land. So, in this case, evolution has been the same in different external environments.

If we believe in an internal tendency, inherent in the living creatures themselves, we do not necessarily have to see the effect of a mysterious force transcending life. Parallelism does not demand this. Let us consider the most striking example, namely the appearance of very high, pillar-like molars with enamel ridges in numerous families of hooved mammals. Their common ancestors had normal molars. The high molars appear at the same time, or at very nearly the same time, in groups as different as horses, bulls, camels, rhinoceroses, and elephants, and at the same time as their size was increasing. It happens as though it were a hidden tendency in the ancestral patrimony, suddenly revealed by the wave of a wand or by some delayed reaction mechanism.

We are familiar with the advantage that the animal has in growing larger. If its food intake increases at the same time as its weight, both its efficiency and speed increase too. But do we fully understand what these simple words "growing larger" imply for a species? Every organ must be remodeled, the teeth as well as the others. And the food intake too has grown larger. If the animal becomes twice as big, then it becomes eight times heavier What will happen if the food intake, too, is multiplied by eight? The crown of the molars, which is the part used in masticating the grass, is only multiplied by four, since it is a surface area. In order to chew a food ration that has been multiplied by eight, the animal will need twice as much time. The proof of this can be seen in large, herbivorous animals like oxen and horses who spend a lot of time grazing in the fields. They spend much more time eating than the average man. In India, elephants can work only four hours a day, because they need the rest of the time for eating.

But to get back to molars. If they work twice as long, they will wear out twice as quickly. So it is not surprising then that their upper parts show the amount of wear, nor that their height increases in a greater proportion than the rest of the body. By becoming longer, the tooth compensates for greater wear.

Parallelism, like convergence, appears here as a particularly striking case of adaptation. And food means environment, so here too, external factors have intervened as well.

The life surrounding us and the creatures flourishing in it are disconcerting. They reflect aspects and forms in which we think we can see certain problems. Then, when we take a closer look, we see other problems arising. In finding the solutions, we find ourselves torn between two sorts of forces. These are the internal forces of the creature itself and the forces of the environment in which the animal lives.

We must have more information. No path should be neglected in our search for truth. And a new path has been opened up in the very tracks of the one we have been following. First we have seen the display of evolutional series of different families of plants and animals, one by one, throughout time. Then, to understand convergences and parallelisms, we have compared the same series in twos. Now, we must group them into larger sets or into populations.

The world of the ancient creatures has many gaps as we see it today. Very few plants and animals have left us evidence. Fossils are rare. So we start dreaming about the world of the past, five or six hundred million years ago. In the haze of our dream, a trawler has set out, with all its sails unfurled, and it has dragged the ocean floor gathering specimens for us. It gathered everything, both beautiful and ugly animals, and tiny and large algae, so that the sample really would be representative of everything. Then, every ten or twenty million years, the trawler would set out again on its cruise, still using the same technique of gathering specimens, so that we might be able to compare the results.

But why dream? The cruise was made and the specimens do exist. They are preserved in rocks and they come to light, thanks to movements in the soil. And the forces that have collected and preserved them, namely the sea, the rivers, and the wind, acted in the same way in past times as they act today. The rocks themselves are the proof of this. We can see the same grains and the same minerals deposited in the same way. At most, they are slightly better consolidated, slightly better cemented together, and a little darker, but what does this matter? The limestone of the Rhineland or of the Ardennes, three hundred eighty million years ago, contained as many shells as the limestone at Paris or Nantes, three hundred thirty million years later. They all resemble one another. From the look of the rocks and the arrangement of their constituents, we know how to recognize different types of environments. In these rocks, there are traces of sea water. In other rocks, there are traces of fresh water, or even land. We have several series (not just one) of comparable samples that have been preserved for us. We can even discern the slightest differences in them and classify them, such as sea with a sandy floor, or a muddy floor, or a coral floor; fresh water or salt water. There are many different choices open to us. Let us start with the most familiar deposits where we shall obtain the most information. These are shallow, sea-water deposits containing a lot of shellfish such as mollusks and brachiopoda. These have been represented since five hundred eighty million years B.C., which was a period when terrestrial plants, for example, had not yet become green.

Now, we shall start work. But how? If we count only the brachiopoda or only the mollusks, or this group of mollusks in particular, we know what we shall learn. The effects of competition, the grandeur and decadence of one group or another, or of an animal empire which was short-lived like all empires, are vicissitudes that we already know. So we shall consider all the competitive animal groups together, as one single block.

Here is the rock containing them, filled with so many shells and imprints that it has been given the name of lumachella, meaning rock of snails, by the Italians. And here, in our quiet libraries, piled up on the shelves where there is never enough room, are works in which the strata have been studied. And there are other works containing lists of species.

For our samples to be valid and comparable, think about the trawler again. Let us compare two strata of the same size and two layers from one era. Do not hope for miracles of uniformity, even in the number of species. Even if we were considering living species, we would see variations. The picture presented by nature today shows a great many variations resulting from the temperature of the water, its salinity, its isolation, and also the type of sea floor on which the animals are lying. Pure, sandy beaches contain fewer animal species than the rocky shores. But let us move from living animals to their remains. The shells have been carried along by currents. Some have been uprooted here, and they have accumulated over there. In addition to this, unfortunately, all areas have not been studied with the same intensity. One stratum has not been investigated as well. One scientist has a tendency to count as species what other scientists would consider as varieties or breeds. Another scientist does too much regrouping.

All these factors allow us to predict very variable numbers of species following the lists. And that is exactly what we find, even if we limit ourselves to one single era. But, in the various strata of one region and one era, the numbers are closely grouped together, at most only being doubled. In order to have comparable data, we shall consider the richest stratum from each era. Basically, this stratum will be the one that benefited from the best conditions, the best water, the best currents, the best sea floor, and the best weather. Now let us look at the results we have obtained.

From one era to another, there are the inevitable high and low points, but what is very surprising is that in spite of so many irregularities and uncertainties, the highs follow a distinctly increasing pattern in the course of time. Around five hundred fifty million years B.C., the record is forty different species in a collection of shells from a stratum in Portugal. Around four hundred seventy-five million years B.C., the record is seventy-nine in Bohemia; around three hundred forty million years B.C., one hundred thirty in England; around two hundred fifty million years B.C., about four hundred in

Sicily; fifty million years B.C., seven hundred thirty-six in the stratum at Bois-Gouet in the Loire-Atlantique department of France. This increase follows a geometric progression, rather than an arithmetic progression. The number of shell fish species on the shores of the ancient seas has doubled on an average of every one hundred million years. Jules Carles, a botanist and philosopher has asked the question, "When we are more more familiar with this progression, will we possess a global curve for the vitality of the living world?"

Think about these results. If the oldest lists are the shortest, it is not because of gaps or destruction. In the strata that were studied, the shells are extremely well preserved and even the slightest details of their ornamentation are still visible. If an unknown cause had made a certain number of species disappear, why would it not have touched the forty others, made of the same minerals or fossilized in the same material? Our results are valid.

These are not the only valid results. Other kinds of deposits, occurring under completely different conditions, show us the same kind of ascending pattern and the same general progression. Here are sea floors of a very fine mud. In them are the imprints of beautiful, exceptionally well preserved fauna, the soft organisms themselves, the roundness of the jelly fish, and the flesh of sea anemones, delicate crustaceans, and sea worms. These are the most beautiful strata in the world. Around five hundred thirty million years B.C., in British Columbia, there were one hundred thirty species. In Bavaria, about one hundred forty-five million years B.C., there were four hundred species in the limestone where the archaeopteryx was found.

And here, found much more frequently, are the marine deposits containing microscopic foraminiferan shells that the oil prospectors like. Around five hundred thirty million years B.C., there were eight species, maybe more; around three hundred fifty million years B.C., forty-two species; around one hundred twenty million years B.C., two hundred fifty species. They have become very abundant.

Now let us go back to the land and gather some green leaves, or rather look at the leaves that nature has gathered for us. Their imprints have been inscribed in stone, in carbon schists, and in the ancient calcareous slime that has now become solidified. The same progression can be found here: twenty-two vascular plant species by three hundred fifty million years B.C.; one hundred fifty by one hundred thirty million years B.C.; five hundred by fifteen million years B.C. Five hundred species is approximately the number that we found today when studying one commune in France.

Insects have no difficulty in avoiding fossilization, not because of their wings, but because they often get eaten. However, strata that do contain insects, and these are often lake deposits, do in fact show us the same type of progression. There were one hundred species around three hundred twenty million years B.C.; two hundred forty around forty million years B.C.; and five hundred sixty around fifteen million years B.C.

In this museum of ours, all the results show similarities. They all show us a progression in the number of plant or animal species throughout the ages. And in all six tables, this increase with its inevitable depressions resembles a geometric progression. In terms of time, we have found for fossil creatures the same type of law that we find for creatures today, when we study them in terms of temperature, salinity, or altitude.

This law is the simplest law imaginable. There is a constant growth rate. The number of species doubles every eighty to one hundred twenty million years. It is a little more for marine fauna living in mud (one hundred eighty to two hundred twenty million years), and it is slightly less for flowering plants and insects (fifty to seventy million years). These results can be given in a different way. In eighty million years, the number of existing species increases by one hundred per cent. In four million years, bearing in mind the compound interest rule, it increases by three to four per cent. During the same period of time, one hundred per cent of new species have appeared, because the life expectancy of one species is four million years on the average. So the species making up the difference of ninety-six to ninety-seven per cent are extinct. In other words, for every thirty new species that appear, twenty-nine disappear. The profit for the living world is only one species. In four million years, this is very little. The living world does not make much of a profit.

The constant growth rate is familiar to all those who have studied the problems of population. If we count individuals, the increased growth is the growth of cultures of bacteria and swarms of flies in the beginning. More generally speaking, it is the increased growth of plant and animal populations of one and the same species, placed in a boundless environment or an environment where the boundaries are still too far distant to be a hindrance.

Populations of species have been subjected to this law, just like populations of individuals who are born one from the other. This is a new and strong proof in favor of their derivation one from the other and of their evolution. For how could we explain such a progression if species had appeared independently? We also see that evolution does not slow down. In five out of six cases, the number of species is still growing, up to this very day. Some people believe, and others have even written, that evolution is over. They claim that the number of species through the ages shows us exactly the opposite tendency. This is the hypothesis of regressive evolution that became popular in France around 1946, but we should reject it. Its supporters believe that all species were created together in the beginning and that since then, their numbers have diminished, because of extinction. This is exactly the opposite of what our sampling showed us.

But let us return to the ancient shores of one hundred fifty million years ago. The same sea breaks over the rocks under the same sky as today, or almost the same. How monotonous the plants and animals are! All the shells we gather are classified into a very small number of species. The rounds are made quickly. Then, in the course of time on the same shores, their differentiation increases, and species become more and more varied. Life tends toward diversity. Other facts have already suggested this.

But think for a moment. If in this period of time, the successive species had been direct opponents, every former species would have succumbed to the new species that was better equipped, just as the small business man today is eliminated by a more modern competitor. And the total number of species would not have increased. Since this is not so and since species have become more numerous, it is because they are more specialized. We have already seen this tendency toward specialization, and now we have the numerical proof of it. If the number of species in the same type of deposit or environment has obeyed a law of geometric progression, it surely did not follow it in a completely rigorous way. There must have been high points, low points, and crises. But at the present state of our research, we cannot distinguish which of these apparent, illusive highs and lows are due to an insufficient number of known strata, or to more detailed study of one stratum than another. Statistics often confront us with this problem of grasp all, lose all. The person who tries to explain too much runs the risk of confusing his explanation. We must always draw fewer conclusions than what we think we see. And it is better to pass over details and stick to the most general tendencies.

The idea of a constant rate of progression shocks some scientists who are inclined to believe in minimums and maximums. They would prefer to see a rapid growth rate to begin with, then a decreased rate. Maybe they are not entirely wrong for the initial period of large groups. Insects and seed plants suggest this. Then, the growth rate does decrease slightly, but it never stops. The number of species, when they are developing, has never tended toward a maximum point in any of the environments studied. Quite the reverse, it continues to grow.

Now we can wonder what happens if we consider the statistical tables of these different environments, or different deposits, such as reefs or mud containing foraminifera, all together instead of separately. Every environment shows a geometric progression first, then perhaps a slight decline. But during the geological ages, new environments opened up to life. The land itself and the air are good examples. And other environments become slightly varied and differentiated because of the new creatures that come to live there. A new tree offers its shade, and new creatures can find shelter there. Hence new progress in the number of species.

Of the two tendencies, slower and faster, which has triumphed? To be able to answer this, we would need complete lists of all the animals and all the plant fossils period by period, over a sufficiently large area that had been studied thoroughly. And this we do have, namely in Great Britain. The different soil periods are well represented. The author, Mr. Etheridge, took care to subdivide his lists into districts and counties when they were too long. Thanks to him, we now have information from known surface areas. Now, if we make the same graphs for these ancient fossils as for present day species, with the number of species in terms of the total surface area of the regions where they were collected, we get a curve of the same type and same inclination as for the species of today.

Now let us examine the collection from which Mr. Etheridge

drew up his lists. There is a new difficulty. Some eras lasted five or ten times longer than others. If they left behind five or ten times more species, what do we conclude? Could an historian usefully compare the total expenditure during Queen Victoria's reign and Edward VIII's reign? One lasted sixty-four years and the other one year. He could obviously compare the annual budgets. Mr. Etheridge was a wise man. He predicted the desires of his future readers. Where his lists become long, he has given subdivisions for the sub-stages and summaries for groups of stages. And this is invaluable for us. Let us look at the numbers he has left us. Since we now know the absolute dates that were not known in his time, we know where to place them on a graph. We shall choose a long era. The axis of abscissas will represent its duration in millions of years, and the axis of ordinates will represent the total number of species found there. We shall do the same for each of the stages and sub-stages into which we have subdivided the era in question. The points obtained can be joined to form a line that is very close to being a straight line. However it is slightly convex toward the top. Where the line cuts the point marking a duration of ten million years, we can read a certain number on the axis of ordinates. This is the number of species that were fossilized in ten million years in the era being studied. We can do the same for the other eras. Then we will have the numbers of species relative to the same duration for every era. It's a long way to Tipperary, according to the song. It has taken even longer to obtain a curve of the number of fossil species in Great Britain. But we have it at last.

From five hundred sixty million years B.C. to six million years B.C., the eve of our present era, we know the number of fossils found in ten million years during the different eras. With the exception of a few irregularities, the curve constantly increases. On the average, we find twenty-eight fossil species around five hundred million years B.C.; one hundred twenty around two hundred eighty million years B.C.; six hundred thirty around one hundred million years B.C.; eleven hundred fifty around six million years B.C. Once again, for the entire population of fossilized species, this is not an arithmetic progression. It is faster. It is a geometric progression. The number of species doubles approximately every eighty million years. For the different environments considered separately, we found ap-

proximately eighty to one hundred twenty million years. So there is
very good harmony.

Would so many distinguished scientists and so many conscientious authors, led by William Smith and Etheridge, who devoted their
lives to studying shells, bones, and the fossil imprints found in
Great Britain and elsewhere, ever have suspected that their results,
when gathered together and compared, would be so concordant with
regard to the number of species identified?

The diversification of larger groups such as phyla or classes has
moved at a different pace throughout time. The number of classes of
terrestrial plants, for example, increased quickly in the beginning and
then slowly. Since the beginning of the Cambrian period, five
hundred eighty million years ago, all the major phyla had already appeared except for vertebrates and vascular plants. This is what had
led some scientists to believe that evolution was over or else approaching its end. As far as phyla are concerned, and they are the
major ramifications of the genealogical tree of species, these scientists are right. Many large branches separated from the trunk very
early, close to the origin of life. Then the speed at which they appeared slowed down. Even today, there are almost no new ones.
But new medium sized and small branches appear, and new leaves
appear abundantly. On the level of species, the tree continues to
grow as rapidly and as beautifully.

The general curve of the fossil species of Great Britain, outside
of its over-all ascension, does show us high and low points. The most
marked drop, where there are only one hundred species, occurred
around two hundred fifty million years B.C. in the Permian period.
This was followed by an upward surge with a peak of twelve
hundred fifty species around one hundred fifty million years B.C.,
during the Jurassic period. Both these features can also be seen in
the curve made from the data published by d'Orbigny in 1850. So
their scope passes beyond Great Britain and extends to Western
Europe at least.

Now we shall risk extending into the distant past the growth
rates established between five hundred million years B.C. and the
present day. If the number of species has doubled every one hundred
million years, the four million species living today would derive

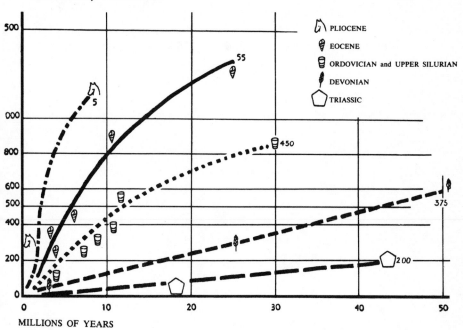

Fossils of the British Isles, according to Philipps (1885). Dating established in 1963. The numbers written at the end of each curve indicate the date of the middle of the period in question.

from a common origin around two billion, two hundred million years B.C. The environment where growth is the slowest is the mud holes where the imprints of soft animals have been found. They would have had only one species then. These values would have been considered excessively bold six years ago. But now that we know of algae and fungi dating from two billion, six hundred million years ago, the above values do not seem so bold. We are tempted to think that more than one species existed around two billion, two hundred million years B.C. So their origin must be even more distant than the retrospective extension of recent dates indicates. It is possible that in the past, the rates were slower, and that more recently, they have been accelerating. But now we are going to see much more distinct signs of acceleration.

PART III

ACCELERATED LIFE

CHAPTER VII

ɟ

Faster and Faster

ɟ

In 1867, when the illustrious Pleiad of biologists and thinkers led by Darwin were flourishing in the British Isles, one of Darwin's disciples, Sir John Lubbock, a reputed ethnologist, summarized his philosophy of human evolution in his work entitled *Man Before History* as follows:

"We are, in reality, only at the threshold of civilization. Far from showing signs that it has reached its end, the tendency for progress seems to have been marked recently by increased audacity and an accelerated speed."

This is the first mention of the acceleration of history of which we know. Five years later, the great French historian Michelet left us this testament in the preface to his last work: "One of the most serious facts, yet one of the least observed, is that the tempo of time has completely changed. It has doubled its pace in a strange way."

In 1948, Daniel Halévy developed the same idea. Like Lubbock and like Michelet, he applied it only to the history of man. But, the year before, a young French philosopher, François Meyer, working alone in Santiago, Chile, had formed the same idea by following a completely different path. His conception was in a much more general form, including the history of life. At about the same time, several French prehistorians arrived at similar viewpoints in their own domain. The idea was in the air. And as often happens in the history of science, it germinated at almost the same time in several different places, just as cement and a pattern of wear appeared at almost the same time in the evolution of the teeth in different families of hooved animals. Just as parallel or convergent evolution can occasionally be seen among the different branches of animal species, so it can be seen in thought. François Meyer, when writing the fundamental pages of *L'Accélération évolutive* ("Evolutionary Acceleration"), was not aware of, or was not thinking of Michelet's words. And Halévy could not have been familiar with Meyer's work. But in the mind of the young philosopher, as in the mind of his venerable elder, a slow maturation had occurred. And we have the fruits of this today.

François Meyer, who was familiar with the classics—and by this we mean the classics of science, of course—decided to take another look at the four stages that Julian Huxley had discerned in the evolution of animals, starting from the primitive unicellular organism: (1) several cells; (2) the head; (3) the lung; (4) warm blood. He researched the probable transition dates in geological history. And he noted that these stages were reached more and more quickly in the course of time. The movement of evolution is an accelerating one.

But only two of Huxley's stages can really be dated. These are the lung and warm blood. The head can only be dated with a great deal of uncertainty. So François Meyer looked elsewhere for control tests.

The first control test was taken from the history of life. It is one of the most important and most typical characteristics of living creatures, namely the chemical composition of their blood and the fluids in which their cells are bathed.

Thus the blood's richness in nitrogen bodies and protein groups increases when we pass from lower animals, such as mollusks, to crustaceans, sharks, and the bony fish that abound in the sea. If we admit that the ancient creatures of the same general structure functioned similarly, as Cuvier's principle proposes, then we can locate in the scale of geological eras the dates when the different increasing protein amounts appeared. And we find a distinct acceleration in recent times.

The acceleration can be seen in the amounts of carbon dioxide, given off during the respiratory cycle for a given change in acidity.

In the interstitial fluids and the blood, there is a balance between the metallic atoms. Some are alkaline, such as sodium and potassium. Others are earthy alkalis such as lime and magnesia. Sometimes one group is dominant, depending on the class of animals. In vertebrates inhabiting the earth or fresh water, the relative proportion of alkalis increases when we pass from fish to amphibians and to reptiles and from there to birds and finally to placental mammals. If we transfer this information to our time chart, once again the progression shows a characteristic acceleration. Thus the evolution of the chemical characteristics of the blood and the interstitial fluids, which can be followed and dated in vertebrates, throughout the geological eras seems to have occurred more and more quickly as we get closer to our own period.

François Meyer has given other examples of acceleration. In vertebrates, one of the most distinct examples is the development of the cerebrum and in particular of the forebrain, which is responsible for intellectual aptitudes. So, naturally, we now ask: "How did the psychology of creatures and the way in which they reacted, evolve in the past?"

The first man to undertake this kind of research was Cuvier. In his investigations on fossil remains, he had established the principle of correlating organs:

"Every organized creature forms a unity. It is a single, sealed system whose parts correspond mutually and cooperate in the same subsequent action. . . ." Whether he uses the word "action" in a broad or narrow sense can be seen in another passage: "A lucky chance helped me prove my idea on the structure of the Anoplotherium's brain [one of the fossils from the Montmartre quarries] . . . . It was not very large, proportionately, and in addition, it was horizontally flattened. Its hemispheres showed no convolutions, but we could see a shallow, longitudinal groove in each hemisphere. All the laws of analogy permitted us to conclude that this animal had no intelligence."

Inferring the animal's functions from its organs is a natural step for the human mind, especially physiological functions involving the organs of fossils. So why can we not infer psychological functions too? If we see tusks and sharp molars in a jaw fossil, we conclude that the animal was probably carnivorous. So, when confronted with a large brain, why should we not admit higher mental aptitudes?

Cuvier discovered the path. Others pursued it. Gaudry in particular showed that throughout the ages, in the subphylum of vertebrates, the forebrain began occupying a larger and larger place. And from this, he concluded that intellience had progressed.

In Germany, the distinguished scientist Rudolf Richter studied the strange traces left by certain worms, and he managed to retrace their comings and goings and to have some understanding of their psychology.

When I turned my attention to these problems, I must admit that it happened without any forethought, while I was reading. My work necessarily made me interested in all aspects of zoology, and animal psychology was among these. But animal psychology had played a very small role in my education as a student, so it was with both curiosity and pleasure that I discovered a fine work written on this topic by J.-C. Filloux. Further reading on this subject confirmed my opinion of this book. The author had adopted a simple, classical, zoological plan, going from the simplest group to the most complex. He had the art of making the progressive development stand out.

The tiny amoeba is able to turn around if it hits a wall. It can also follow a prey. A worm, if placed at the entrance of a T-shaped tunnel, can learn to choose the branch where it will find food and to avoid the one where an electric shock awaits it at the end. The chimpanzee knows how to use a stick to knock down a banana, and if the stick is not long enough, it can join bamboos together. Between these two aptitude levels, there are countless intermediates that Filloux has described.

Then I studied the variations of certain abilities in terms of time from the most distant geological eras. And I had the idea of examining animal psychology from this point of view. As I had already found several different types of variations in other domains, some accelerated, and some at a constant rate, I had no preconceived ideas on what sort of variations I would find here. However, I thought it was wiser to let someone else make the final choice of data. I drew up a provisional list of eighteen aptitude levels from the simplest to the most complex. I numbered them from one to fifty, purposely leaving blank numbers in between to represent intervals and to allow for future modifications without having to use halves and quarters. Then I asked two of my associates, J.-C. Filloux himself, and B. Guillemain, author of a learned philosophical dissertation, if they would kindly give me their opinions of it. Should some levels be omitted, should others be added, should the order be changed, or should there be changes in the intervals? Naturally, to avoid any preconceived ideas, I did not tell them how I intended to use this table. They gave me their wise opinions. Mostly, they coincided with mine. Where they did not agree with me, I used the average between our differences. At their request the scale was extended to fifty-five. In its final form, it was more their work than mine.

Then what I did was simple. At every level of the scale, I noted the zoological groups able to reach that level. Then, in works written about fossils, I looked for the date when their first representative had appeared in the past. Then I made a graph with the dates on the axis of abscissas and the aptitude levels on the axis of ordinates. Hence the curve obtained is a curve of mental variations in terms of time. It was like doing in psychology what Meyer had done in anatomy and physiology. When a geologist finds an ant fossilized in amber, he does not doubt for a single moment that its internal anatomy and its physiology resemble the anatomy and physiology of ants today. He does not imagine it as resembling the anatomy and physiology of crabs or frogs. And likewise for its habits, customs, and reactions.

With regard to this aptitude scale, it would probably have been better to have based it on measurable abilities. But at the present time, we do not know of any suitable ones. In the meanwhile, we have resorted to these qualificative levels described above. This method has been tested elsewhere. For example, this is how the hardness of minerals and precious stones is evaluated and how the intensity of earthquakes is measured.

But we have only one regret. It would have been better if we had used one and the same test for the whole range of aptitudes.[1]

[1] This is the only objection made by Teilhard de Chardin when he was told of this test.

Unfortunately, the amoeba's ability to turn around or to chase prey is just a game for all the upper animals, and it would not permit us to establish classifications among them. And on the other hand, the chimpanzee's ability to link bamboos in order to make a longer stick is completely beyond all other animals, even other monkeys. So we have not yet found a test that is applicable from one end to the other of the animal series.

The solution possible at the present time is therefore the sort of scale that we adopted. The results, when put into table form, follow a regular pattern. First there is the amoeba with simple reactions. Then there are sponges attached to rocks, apparently rigid, but yet excitations can be transmitted very gradually. There are sea anemones whose tentacles all converge together on the prey, even if only one tentacle has been stimulated. Jellyfish show more varied responses. Then there are starfish, and there are the worms that can choose the right direction in a T-shaped tube. All these aptitude levels, numbered from one to twelve, are reached at an ancient date, somewhere between three billion, five hundred million and six hundred million years B.C. From number fourteen upward, all the aptitude levels are reached after six hundred million years B.C., and with very few exceptions, in an order demonstrating increasing development. This is new evidence in favor of evolution and is parallel to the evidence we have already discovered in the anatomy of the organism. The evolution of the body on the one hand, and the evolution of reactions and psychology on the other, have moved hand in hand. All in all, the psychology has evolved in one direction toward increased complexity, like so many other characteristics in the history of living creatures.

When we examine this in more detail, we find some strange coincidences. Consider, for example, the two phyla of articulates and vertebrates. Although they are structurally very different, their average aptitude levels are reached at more or less the same eras. Cockroaches capable of completing test sixteen, which is the maze test, appear after fish who stop at test fourteen, and before upper reptiles who are capable of performing the various aptitudes tested at level twenty. So there are convergences in psychological evolution just as there are in anatomical evolution. But then, the articulates rarely pass twenty, while vertebrates go much further.

Men differ psychologically according to where they live. A country man does not think or react in the same way as a townsman. A highlander differs in mentality from a lowlander or a sailor. Is this the same for animals, keeping the same proportions and making the necessary transpositions? In effect, the first ten psychological levels were reached by creatures living in water. The following levels, from ten to sixteen, were reached by mixed groups. Level eighteen and above, with no exceptions, were reached only by land creatures, probably because the land, in the diversity of its countryside and the abundance of different species, confronts living species with more varied stimuli, to which several responded with a greater reaction scale.

Since our aptitude scale has so far produced very plausible results, we are inclined to believe the next characteristic it shows us. In the course of time, the various levels have been reached more and more quickly. The representative curve does not form a straight line. In more recent times, it climbs higher and higher. So what law is it obeying? Our first thought is a constant rate of progression for the aptitude levels but the curve keeps climbing and the rate is not constant. The law it follows is a different one, and it is a surprising one. To make the representative line a straight line, the best method is to maintain an arithmetic progression for the performance levels, but to take a decreasing geometric progression for the time they take to achieve these levels. In other words, make a logarithmic scale. Every group of two aptitude levels is reached almost twice as quickly as the group preceding it.

Naturally it is very tempting to extend the part of the curve situated between six hundred million years B.C. and the present day into the distant past. Thus, for the first creature capable of reacting, we find a starting date somewhere between one billion, eight hundred million and five billion years B.C., and this seems compatible with all the other information we know about the age of the earth. Since this is the last piece of information of this type that we have, we shall now give a résumé of our findings.

Starting Dates	*Millions of Years B.C.*		
Expansion of the universe, according to astronomers	12,000	to	14,000
Earth-Moon system, following the slowing of the			
rotation of the earth (Chevallier and Cailleux)	3,300	to	3,500
Terrestrial lead, according to Holmes	3,300	to	3,500
The oldest mineral lepidolite (lithia mica)			3,360
Consolidation of the first continental shelves	2,600	to	4,200
Algae in the ancient soil that is now Canada			2,600
Living creatures following the longevity of classes			
and orders, etc.	2,000	to	5,000
Creatures able to react	1,800	to	5,000
Different animal or plant species	2,200	or	more
Unicellular animals (Huxley's stages)	2,000	to	4,000
Imprints of soft animals in fine mud	2,200	or	more
Plants with cells that are all alike	950	or	more

We see that the history of life has its roots deeply in the past. If we consider the enormous uncertainties involved in some of these estimates, stemming from the fact that twenty-five years ago no absolute dating had yet been established, we are still amazed by the similar results obtained from so many different methods. We hope that some of these methods will be developed further in the future, so the results will be even better.

Now this question arises. In our scale, where is man situated with his ability to react, to resolve problems, and to surmount difficulties?

Some people may be appalled at the idea of making graphs and equations of the human mind and reducing man to the level of an animal. But our purpose is quite different. In man, there is a distinction between the body, the mind, and the soul. The word "soul" we are using here in the sense it was given by Christian theologians and philosophers. And what we are representing here in numbers and graphs does not apply to the soul but to the mind. This is not an act of irreverence. In other words, we are using the old distinction between *animus* and *anima*.

Among the fossils that we have of the bodies of animals and men, there are some transitions that are so borderline that we hesitate whether to classify some creatures, such as the Australopithecus and the Australopithecus transvaalenis (South African man), as higher monkeys or primitive men. We have the choice, but we do not know where to place the limit. And even if we do manage to establish a limit some day, it will be a very tenuous limit.

As far as the mind is concerned, we must clarify our statements. In the first place, the people who are reading this book, and the person who wrote it, are men, not chimpanzees. This is a major factor. But we should not be dazzled by it, nor should we become excessively arrogant about it. Animals, in their own way, do have a mind too. All perceptive people who have raised animals know this. Other people, when speaking of a dog that they understand, and which understands them, say, "It can do everything but talk." This thought is more profound than it seems, if it is true that talking implies the faculty of abstraction.

But do we wish for more formal, more scientific proofs of the existence of a mind in animals? Let us go to one of the laboratories where scientists are studying the psychology of rats. Over here, a rat has been able to perform the following test. To obtain food, it must pull a cord, like the rope on a bell. But instead of a bell, there is an open box that revolves and drops a slug. The rat takes the slug between its teeth and pushes it into the slit of a slot machine. It receives the desired food. Monkeys have even been conditioned to receive different food for slugs of different colors. There is one color for grapes, another color for water, and still another to obtain permission to jump on the shoulders of their trainer—and above all, they prefer the blue slugs which are worth two pieces of fruit, as opposed to the white slugs which are worth only one piece.

But let us come back to the simple rats. One rat alone in its cage has been trained to obtain its food by depressing a lever. At every tap, the machine drops a pellet of food. At first, the machine was placed right beside the lever. When the rat was quite used to the way it worked, the machine was placed at the other end of the cage. The poor rat was very taken aback. It hesitated. Then it found it. It pushed the lever, then went to the opposite end of the cage to eat the pellet that had just dropped.

When it had fully acquired this skill, it was taken out of the cage, and a second rat was put in its place and trained in the same way. Then in turn, the second rat was taken out of the cage, and a third rat was trained in the same way. All three rats had been trained separately.

Then came the experimenter's master stroke. When all three rats had been trained, he put all three of them in the cage together. When they began to get hungry, what happened? One of the rats went and depressed the lever. At the other end of the cage, a pellet dropped, but another rat ate it. The same rat resentfully started again, and the other two rats continued to get the profits of its work.

But finally, the hungry rat found the solution. It depressed the lever three times in a row, then happily went to eat the third pellet that was free.

As the experiment continued, the other two rats also understood what was happening, but they showed no eagerness to work the lever themselves, preferring to leave the work to their more zealous pal. In short, they were shirkers! From rats to men—it is not far. All in all, we see that there are some comparable psychological facts in animal and man. And it is these facts and only these facts that we wish to compare here.

Those who are still worried about the distinction between mind and soul in man should bear in mind the cases of wolf children in India. These are human children, raised by a she-wolf, living like wolves, and not speaking. The minister who found them did not hesitate to baptize them, and every priest would have done likewise. Similarly, in the case of lunatics, their minds have failed but their souls are just as dear to God as the souls of healthy men. Without going so far, we ourselves, all of us, were once fetuses, then young children, before becoming men, and we passed through stages where we had a psychology similar to that of lower, then upper animals. At eleven months old, we were approximately at the level of chimpanzees. All psychologists agree on this point. At that age, our minds were certainly less developed and less capable than they are today. Did we have souls?

All laboratory research has led us to place the division between chimpanzees and men, and not between any of the different races of man. All the different races of man have the faculty of abstraction. All can separate the subject and the object, which are used to clarify man's perception. All have a notion of the distant future, and no animal has any real knowledge of this, not even those with the instinct to hoard food supplies. And finally, all races of man today have a language, where their faculty of abstraction manifests itself. These languages contain at least several thousand words, of which five hundred are used by peasants. On the other hand, among farm-yard animals, hens only have seven different squawks.

Also, psychologists all agree that there is a greater interval between man and the chimpanzee than there is between the chimpanzee and his immediate follower, the orangutan. In the scale that I gave to J.-C. Filloux and B. Guillemain, they indicated the following intervals: from the gorilla to the orangutan, two, which is the usual interval for lowel levels; from the orangutan to the chimpanzee, four; from the chimpanzee to man, about twelve, insofar as we can evaluate it.

Now we must find the corresponding point on the graph and try to determine at what period in prehistoric times man began to manifest the psychological aptitudes of present-day man. We have several methods of discovering this, particularly in traces of art and industry, and also in the internal molds of skulls, which give us an idea about the cerebrum. There is beautiful art, dating from twenty thousand years before our era, in the caves at Altamira and in Perigord. Skulls similar to ours date from one hundred thousand or two hundred thousand years ago. Cut stone, in a very corroded state, has been found dating from more than a million years ago. The first chimpanzees date from a period between eight and twenty million years ago, so the time interval between the appearance of the chimpanzee and the appearance of man can thus be established at between seven and twenty million years.

In our graph, we note that man is placed exactly on the extension of the graph of all the animals. The progression that begins with them continues in man, and is accentuated there, still following the same law.

From the amoeba to the sea anemone, to the bee and to man, the history of life is a relay race, where the torch is passed from hand to hand, and finally to us. It is man's time. The law of acceleration, visible in the evolution of animals, leads directly to him. And he is the first to be aware of it.

✦

The Theories of Evolution

✦

Evolution is a great and wonderful problem: one hundred to four hundred million of the most varied plant and animal species following after each other on the face of the earth and in the water for three billion years. Each of these species lasts for an average of four million years, which is ten thousand times longer than the Roman empire lasted. And, in spite of this extraordinary stability, this world becomes renewed very gradually. Old species evolve by engendering new species. For every thirty species that appear, only one, as we have seen, contributes to increasing the population. The other twenty-nine disappear for ever.

How do species appear? And how do they become extinct? Basically, we do not know the essentials and we are hesitant. The best minds do not agree. As the theories are occasionally quite abstract, we shall explain them by giving examples as often as possible. And each theory will be presented in its best light and in its most recent form.

To start, let us go to the nearest swamp. We can see a furtive figure walking through the reeds. It is a heron with a long bill. It is very strangely built with its long legs. So we wonder where herons have come from. Every evolutionist will admit that the heron is derived from a bird with normal legs. But how and by what mechanism did this lengthening occur?

Modern Lamarckians tell us: "This bird, by frequenting swamps, had the habit of stretching its legs. This caused a modification in its hormones, which are specific chemical substances capable of long-

range action and which play such a great role in all of our functions." Distributed throughout the whole body of the heron, hormones have been able to have an influential action on the eggs as on
the rest of the heron's body, and they have produced a parallel
change, namely the capacity to have longer legs. This lengthening
evolved later in the chick and then in the adult.

Darwinians, however, have a different point of view. "Among the
various birds, there were some individuals with longer legs and other
individuals with shorter legs in the swamps. Those with the longer
legs, were better suited to their environment because of their legs,
and in the competition, they triumphed. This was natural selection."

Then the supporters of the idea of mutation intervene: "Abrupt
changes or mutations appear at random. They occur mainly in the
genes, which are tiny particles joining together to form chromosomes,
and chromosomes are the essential part of the cell nuclei. Some
mutations are good and work in favor of the species. Others are
bad. Natural selection operates between these mutations, and the
good ones are kept."

The Lamarckian and the supporter of mutation have explained
how the heron's long legs were formed and why they were conserved.
The Darwinian explained why they were conserved, but he hardly
touched on how they appeared.

According to the Lamarckian, the swamp water plays a fundamental role. It causes the heron to react, and the reaction is the
appearance of long legs. According to the Darwinian and the supporter of mutation, the swamp water plays no role in the appearance
of the heron's long legs. It plays a role only in their conservation
and their selection.

The Lamarckian admits that the lengthening of the heron's legs,
once it has appeared in one heron, can be transmitted to its descendants, or at least partly transmitted in certain cases. That is to
say, acquired characteristics are hereditary. The direct disciples of
Darwin admit this too, but the supporters of mutation emphatically
reject it. Only random mutations are hereditary according to them.

The heron is like a rich man, whose great-grandparents were
poor. According to Lamarck's doctrine, his wealth was earned by the
work of several generations. According to Darwin's theory, the
wealth was obtained after some successful business ventures, in

which the family eliminated its competitors. For the supporters of mutation, this wealth was won in an enormous lottery.

The Lamarckian will freely admit that the heron's legs could gradually have got longer from generation to generation; so will the Darwinian. But according to the supporters of mutation, the modification had to occur suddenly. If we think we can see continuous transitions in the course of time, as, for example, in the paludinas of Lake Levantin, it is only because they are masking a series of small, sudden mutations, all occurring in the same direction.

When confronted with such markedly diverging opinions, we wonder how they originated. They are partly related to eras, and, we guess, even to the personality of the scientist. Lamarckism was the first doctrine, dating from 1802. The creature's reaction to its environment can be seen in the wading birds whose legs lengthened from frequenting swamps, but this reaction can also be seen in Lamarck himself, with all due respect. To make a living, he was forced to be a soldier, a bank clerk, and a clerk coping with administrative problems. Then he became a botanist, and at the age of fifty he accepted a zoological position. Until then, he had been a supporter of the theory of immutability, but he did not hesitate to become an evolutionist. How could such a man not have believed in the creature's effort to become adapted to his environment?

For Darwin, who put forward his doctrine fifty years later, environment did not play a very great role, or at least it was hardly an obstacle. Darwin traveled, then retired in seclusion, living off his annuities. At that period, this was a normal life for anyone of his social position. We know the reverberations the ideas of selection and competition caused in his country. The creature whose only problem is to assert himself and whose every innovation stems from himself and not from the environment is not only the heron, but is also the Englishman of the Victorian era, isn't it?

The theory of mutation originated a half-century later. If chance plays a role, it is because the very fact of the mutations demonstrates it. And since 1950, the theory, in its recent form, has acknowledged a large random factor, extending it to the whole geological past and to all evolution. This is in agreement with a very strong similar tendency in physics, astronomy, and many other aspects of contemporary science.

Finally, the form of Lamarckism appearing around 1950 with Bourdier, Dechambre, and Wintrebert is based on hormones, organizing molecules, and the chemistry of the body. In this respect it also follows modern tendencies.

When dealing with practical problems, these three doctrines do not take the same attitude. To obtain useful, new plant and animal varieties, the supporters of mutation and the Darwinians rely exclusively on crossbreeding and selection. Lamarckians consider this too, but they also include the effect of the environment, such as transplantation and acclimatization. In this respect, Lamarckism is more open and flexible. The idea of mutation and Darwinism rely on chance and on death. They are hard and fatalistic. Lamarckism has confidence in life. It is optimistic.

At the present time, most Anglo-Saxons believe in the idea of mutation. The French tend toward Lamarckism. The Russians, too, favor Lamarckism, which fits in well with the Marxist doctrine. But there are exceptions. For example, Prenant, a Marxist, believes in the idea of mutations. And on the other hand, the English and Americans have recently produced some very good evidence in favor of Lamarckism.

Now that we are aware of the doctrines and their implications, we will be able to apply them better to the evidence impartially left for us by the fossils.

Let us go back to the most distant past and take a look at the possible role of selection and mutation in the history of life, following its progress, triumphs, and distinct tendencies toward creatures that are larger, more lasting, more complex, more specialized, and more diversified.

Natural selection and sexual selection have certainly played a large role in the disappearance of individuals and plant and animal species and in the preservation or ascension of other species. As a general rule, the most suited creatures have had more chance of surviving.

On the other hand, the appearance of new forms poses a difficult problem. Darwinism does not deal with it. Lamarckism offers us a lot of probabilities but very few facts that can be seen working in nature today. The theory of mutation supplies us with a heap of

Fish fossil from the Eocene epoch.—Photo Michel Cachoux

detailed variations, but few of these are important or useful variations. It is like making a mountain out of a molehill. The little drosophila fly (fruit fly) which holds the record for mutations today, hardly varied throughout the geological eras. Fifty million years ago, it was represented by the same genus as today. On the other hand, the horse provides us with very few present-day mutations, yet its lineage was extremely variable throughout the ages. There were eight or ten genera of horses in fifty million years. Was this because of random misfortune?

But this is more important. We know that the great majority of mutations are bad. We can even see this exemplified in our own flesh, or at least the flesh of other men. Most congenital defects are of this origin. So to explain evolution and the progress of life throughout time by a process where defects and imperfections are dominant seems paradoxical. Resorting to selection attenuates the paradox, but does it erase it? The explanation for a sonata is not in a series of wrong notes.

And this is even more important. If it is true that evolution results from random mutations at a constant rate throughout the geological eras, then we should have more chance of observing traces of it when there is a short period of time between generations. If evolution really begins with a lottery and if we take a ticket each time, the main prize should be won more often as the drawings become more frequent. However, the drawing, or new generation, is every several years for horses and elephants. For the tiny diatoms, it is every few days. And yet the main prize, which is the new species, does not appear more often in the course of the geological eras. The life expectancies are the same in both cases.

In a lottery or in a raffle, we have more chance of winning the big prize if there are one hundred tickets than if there are one hundred thousand. Life offers us this variety. Some species have very few seeds or eggs. Others have a great many. Oysters have several million, and puffballs have several billion. It is true that many of these seeds are lost or eaten while they are still at the egg stage or unfertilized. But many also become larvae, then young organisms, and are then subjected to selection as are the adults. We should find more rapid evolution where there are more eggs. But the picture of life in the past shows us nothing of the kind. The fresh water mussel called the unio lays two hundred thousand eggs a year. The related viviparous paludina gives birth to only fifty offspring. Yet, in the geological strata, it is the paludina that has evolved more quickly than the unio. The camel gives birth to one offspring per year. The frog gives birth to five thousand. Five thousand tadpoles abounding in the water of a pond—what a magnificent opportunity for selection! And yet, in the geological strata, it is the camel that has evolved more quickly.

The lottery is not sufficient. The theory of mutation is a failure in two respects. The evolution of the species cannot result from chance alone, even if selection corrected the mistakes. Nor can it result only from the inward effort of creatures, because the more creatures there are at a given time, the more efforts they would make; hence there would be rapid evolution. And this is not the case. Something else outside the creature must have played a part too.

Lecomte du Nouÿ distinguished the time of organized creatures, or individual time, and the time of events. All in all, the evolution of plants and animals has been regulated, not by individual time, but by the time of events, and it has followed this constant rhythm. It is closely linked with the evolution of the rest of nature, which is strictly controlled by the environment. Life is intimately connected with the environment.

And so our tour through the past tends to make us believe more and more that new species originated, in the course of time, from the creatures' reaction to the environment in which they lived as Lamarck had suggested a long time ago. But some species could also have originated by crossbreeding, by the multiplication of chromosomes, and even (and why not?) by mutation, or by the modification of the genes of the nuclei. Genes are a definite reality. They have a fundamental role in the determination of small characteristics. There are many ways of reconciling them with Lamarckism. Here is one, proposed by the French biologist Wintrebert, which he calls "chemical Lamarckism."

Genes undergo two main types of modification. Some occur at random, and the others are directed or Lamarckian. Random modifications are the mutations that are generally disastrous and are generally eliminated by selection. The other modifications are due finally to the environment. In response to the environment, the living creature engenders hormones or antibodies or other substances which act simultaneously on its somatic cells, its germ cells, and on the genes. Because of their very origin, these modifications would obviously favor the living creature, and selection would assure their pre-eminence.

Finally it is possible that the characteristics first inscribed only in the genes, do come to be inscribed in the basic mass of the egg-cell also. This would explain why the egg cell controls the development of the essential characteristics of the groups as we have seen in crossed fertilizations between sea urchins and starfish. So the gene appears as one of the necessary intermediaries between the external environment on the one hand and the egg mass on the other. But it is an extremely reticent and slow intermediary. The gene is a traditional museum curator, who is impervious to change. Immutable and authoritarian in manner, he accepts innovations only under persistent pressure from his director and the public, and he is prone to bursts of ill humor without rhyme or reason and almost always without consequences. These are mutations.

Have these bursts of ill humor played a large role in the history of his museum? Have random mutations played a large role in the history of life?

The future will tell us.

✓

Conclusion

✓

Life appeared on earth three or four billion years ago. It was derived from inorganic matter, or at least everything indicates that it was. Even today, the simplest organisms, viruses, can be living one moment, then stiff and crystallized the next. The smallest viruses are made of one single molecule.

Evolved from the physical environment, life has since remained in close contact with it. The distribution of creatures and the speed of their evolution have been greatly influenced by it. Life's major crises have also been the crises of the physical environment. The glaciations of the Permian period and the Quaternary era are evidence of this.

Living creatures have become adapted to their environment and adjusted to their way of life and to their surroundings. B. Cuenot spoke of: "Adaptation, this frightening problem. . . ." It is only frightening for those believing in random mutations. But for the Lamarckian, it is very simple. By interacting with its environment, the creature reacts and adapts, or else it disappears. The problem of adaptation is part of the problem of existence.

Marine creatures have been able to become terrestrial creatures only by maintaining internally a part of the original liquid environment in their blood or in their sap. The late Yugoslavian biologist, Giaja, rightly concluded: "It is not the organism that has become adapted to the surrounding environment; on the contrary, it has adapted the environment." We think of Bernard Shaw's words: "The reasonable man adapts himself to the world: the unreasonable one persists in trying to adapt the world to himself. Therefore all progress depends on the unreasonable man."

Giaja's notes, too, that warm blood, a recent acquisition (one hundred fifty million years old, perhaps), makes the organism independent of the changes in the external environment. "This is avoiding the issue rather than becoming adapted." And he adds: "In reality and fundamentally, life has only a restricted adaptation power. The basis of life is too close to physico-chemistry, and the notion of adaptability is foreign to this. Adaptation is not a primordial quality of life. It is secondary and is attached to the organization of living creatures."

It is also attached to their evolution. The real and great tendency of life is to last and to reproduce. Self-perpetuation; becoming larger, more complex, and more specialized; the addition of new acts to the repetitive ancestral history; self-reproduction; self-continuation through a lineage of germ cells and through creatures that will be engendered in a self-likeness, but not necessarily similar to the distant ancestors: these are the characteristics of life. Life evolves, and the species engender one another.

Their domains overlap both in time and in space like the paths of molecules in a gas or like the footsteps of people walking in a park. But if we look back and consider the large groups, then we see quantitative numerical laws. In space, biologists have shown that these are logarithmic laws, completely similar to the law linking air pressure and altitude. Like the molecules of a gas, species react with each other, tending toward a global equilibrium.

From six hundred million years ago until today, there are some remarkable constants. For example, the life span of species has hardly varied. It has only oscillated between one and eight million years on the average.

The number of species has grown following the most simple law that could be imagined *a priori*. It has grown at an almost constant rate, following the rule for calculating compound interest. It has doubled approximately every one hundred million years. Today the number of species is approximately four million. Thus, throughout time, life has tended toward diversification. The growth is perceptible right up to the most recent times and it is not slowing. Evolution has no limits, nor has it stopped. Those who have claimed that it has stopped have been judging by vague, qualitative, personal impressions. The proof of numbers is our best contradiction of their assertions.

There is a fourth type of variation that Lecomte du Nouÿ did not foresee. The main stages of life have accelerated throughout time. These main stages are, namely, progress in the structure, chemistry, and psychology of animals. The aptitude levels that can be discerned by their reactions are reached more and more quickly. They lead directly to man, and with man, this acceleration has become very striking today, especially technically and scientifically speaking.

Man's relationship with the rest of life, already seen in the chemistry of his body, in his cells, in his organs and their functions, has been confirmed by the whole history of life since its beginning. Not so long ago, the resemblance between monkey fossils and human fossils was so great that we were not sure where to place the division.

Which creature or thing, over the centuries, has tended to become more complex, more specialized, larger and more victorious? Is it the creatures whose head is the most developed? Does it occur when time plays a large role? Who wants to go faster and faster? Who wants to last and be perpetuated? Who is looking for immortality? Is it life? Or is it humanity? The history of life foreshadows our history.

Our relationship and our filiation with plants and animals, which the study of fossils has illustrated so well, was felt a long time ago by men. They are expressed most poetically in the religions of men and in their philosophies. How noble the ancient Greeks and the Hindus are in their abstention from eating meat and fish, out of respect for living creatures. In the deserts of the Orient, the Semites searched their consciences about this, and they had to have a decree from the Lord God in person to consecrate their right to be masters over animals. Modern leaders and their deputies use less tact today in dominating men.

In the book of Genesis, God spoke to Noah and to his sons: "And I, behold, I establish my covenant with you, and with your seed after you; and with every living creature that is with you, of the fowl, of the cattle, and of every beast of the earth with you, from all that go out of the ark, to every beast of the earth."

Plant fossil from the Carboniferous period.—Photo François Garnier

Saint Francis of Assisi had a wolf for a friend, and he called it his brother.

The Christian believes that God is a father. Modern science, by showing us the filiation between the inorganic and the living and between the living and man, is opening boundless horizons to man's faith.

In the history of every creature and of every species, it is very difficult to estimate the extent of external and internal forces. When a law or a fact does not seem explicable by external forces (for example, the very long antlers of the Irish deer fossil), we are tempted to call upon internal forces. And from here, it is only a short step to attributing to life a secret force. Many people have taken this step, attracted by the aura of mystery. In fact, the vital force is mainly the screen formed by our ignorance. Medicine abounds in examples illustrating that what was considered a vital force yesterday is now explained by hormones, antibodies, or by humoral interactions.

In this respect, the study of internal forces is wholesome and beneficial. But to proclaim that the unknown cannot be known, and to turn our ignorance into a form of vitalism, will certainly assure the downfall of this vitalism. The history of biological sciences has amply proved this. If life does have a special force, a soul, we do not see why it would be denied the small task of organizing all development from the frog's egg to the active molecule of sterols to the hydrogen atom, which is a world in itself. If there is a problem, it is posed for all creatures at the same time, and it is posed only once.

The same impression (and it is only an impression, not a certainty) is valid for all functions and for the goals. There are so many obstacles and so many enemies threatening the young that the female sea urchin needs ten million eggs to hope to produce one sea urchin from them. The liver flukes need five billion eggs to produce at least one liver fluke. But they have these millions and billions of eggs. Did nature take some wise precautions? As Prenant notes: "Would a factory worker be considered skilled if he boasted of successfully completing one part out of every five billion?" Do we see a special proof of the existence of God in the sudden growth of sea snails sixty million years ago? Do we say that our insectivorous ancestors, by learning to fly at about the same time, had in mind the future expansion of humanity? Were they happy about the good turn they were doing to other animal groups, their competitors, like a businessman who is selling a new product?

Are we disappointed? Has this life which we cling to turned out to be a mechanism, a computation, or nothing? Aragon said: "Read love in the eyes and not in numbers." Is life only numbers?

Here Lecomte du Nouÿ comes to the rescue. He tosses some atoms about at random and puts forward this challenge: "Can I obtain a living creature in this way, a sea urchin for example?" And he concludes: "The living creature is a miracle."

He forgets that his reasoning can be applied just as well to a granite rock as to the sea urchin that dug its hole in the rock. He forgets that life, above all, is a history and that creatures do not come into the world as a lottery prize. Look at the male and female sea urchins living in the hollow of a rock that is washed by the waves. It is highly likely that they will emit virgin eggs and fertilizing cells. It is highly probable that young sea urchins will be born from these unions. In this water, abounding in eggs, it would be hard for them not to be born. And it was the same for their parents and likewise for all their ancestors, since the time when living organisms first appeared on earth. Lecomte du Nouÿ's conclusion possibly has a point, but it has this point only for the first organism, the first virus, the first genes, or for the first molecule capable of remodeling matter to its own form. Once again, history has brought us back to the very origin of life.

Now the physicist wishes to speak: "In the closed circuit systems that I study in my laboratory, everything, when left to itself, heads toward the greatest disorder. Is this the same for the living world?" And now many men raise their heads and speak of the order and the harmony of life. Yet the particular order that they believe they see in life can be contested. There are four million different species swarming around today, and their domains and ways of life overlap in an infinite number of ways. Is this order? Would there not be as much order, and even more, if living matter were distributed in only two or three well-adapted, well-balanced, immutable plant and animal species? It would make natural science dissertations much simpler. Even this book would be much shorter. A Russian scientist, Kostitzin, notes that in the totality of the universe, "the development of an improbable condition is not impossible, and the nondevelopment of such a condition is not very probable." Even if life is "an ascending series of improbable events, it remains strictly in agreement with the calculations of probabilities." And before him, the French mathematician, Emile Borel, had shown that life's order is achieved at a cost of greater disorder and an enormous waste of energy.

In the past, men have been tempted to admire the order and harmony of nature. They were taking the exception as the rule. On the one hand, there is the order, harmony, and ascension of successful creatures, and on the other, there is the defeat and death of those that fall. A million young oysters are eaten or killed for every one that develops. The massacre of innocent creatures is eternal. The seal kills fish, the bird kills insects, and the ox kills the grass. The history of life has shown us peaks and depressions. It has shown us the end of trilobites, ammonites, and giant reptiles. Competition and war are its main laws.

Claude Bernard has talked about "this slaughter that we ironically call the harmony of nature." And we too, as men, in our airplanes, when we kill women and children, or when we burn their villages in the name of our country or our civilization, we are guilty. The idea of original sin can be seen in its fullest expression in modern biology.

The struggle is the great law of life for plants and animals. Darwin writes: "From nature's war, from famine, and from death has come the noble end that we can conceive, namely the development of upper animals." Obviously the author and the readers of this book are classified among these upper animals.

The Marxist philosopher sees the struggle in nature, the interaction and the evolution, and from it he tries to draw rules that are applicable, if possible, to human societies. This rational attitude is a very great force for the Marxist.

The Christian sees the fight, and he challenges it. He looks at it head on and says: "There is something else which is its counterpart, namely love. And this other thing must win."

It is a strange fact that the Christian, not the Marxist, is the most rebellious. If the Marxist were a revolutionary right to the end, he should think like a true Christian. In the discords of nature and the struggle and the evil tearing it apart, the Christian finds one of his strongest reasons for believing in a better world: a supernature, or another kingdom where love triumphs.

The diversity of ways of thinking are as great as the diversity of species. Everyone is free. You will be able to understand, each in your own way, the history of life. You will be able to go to the cliffs and the quarries and see the bones, the shells, and the imprints inscribed in stone, as we have done here. You will be able to question them about the earth, our mother, about her history and her past.

And to the creatures which used to live on earth's beaches and to the flowers which used to live under earth's sky, I would like to say thank you for what you have taught us.

Les Moutiers-en-Retz
1958–1963

GLOSSARY OF TERMS

Glossary of Terms

A

ACCELERATION—Increase in speed during the course of time. Strictly speaking, there is acceleration when stages of equal length (or aptitudes of the same level) are reached in a shorter and shorter time. Specific case: the times of these stages form a decreasing geometric progression. Each stage is reached n times more quickly than the preceding stage. Examples from the history of life: the main stages in the anatomical development of animals, as outlined by Julian Huxley: the mental aptitude levels in the animal series up to man.—(Etymology: Latin *celer*, rapid.)

AMOEBA—Microscopic unicellular animal perpetually changing its shape: one of the simplest known forms of animal life found in nature today. It measures one tenth of a millimeter. It lives in water or in damp ground.—(Etym: Greek *amib*, change.)

AMMONITE—One of the groups of cephalopod mollusks, characterized by folded suture lines and lobes that stand out. Lived from the Devonian period through the Cretaceous. Comprises a large number of families, genera, and species. The species are relatively easy to recognize, and some lived only a million or a half million years, and so they are excellent fossils characteristic of an era.—(Etym: resembling the horns of the Egyptian god *Ammon*.)

AMPHIBIA—A class of vertebrates, intermediate in many characters between fish and reptiles. In reality, made of several very distinctive orders. Exists since the Devonian period. Present-day example: the frog.—(Etym: Greek *bi*, ife, and *amphi*, of both kinds: they are adapted for both land and water.)

AMPHIOXUS—A small animal resembling a worm and living in the sand on beaches. It belongs to the superphylum of chordates. It has

213

a stiff yet flexible axis extending along its back; a dorsal nervous system; respiratory slits on the sides of the neck. These are all the characteristics that it shares with vertebrates, but it is a protochordate. It has no cranium, no vertebrae, and its brain is only a simple swelling.—(Etym: Greek *ox*, sharp, and *amphi*, of both kinds: both the head and tail are pointed.)

ARCHAEOPTERYX—The oldest known bird. It already had wings and feathers. But it was still very like the reptiles with claws on each wing and its very long tail. It dates from the upper Jurassic period. —(Etym: Greek *arch*, first, old, and *pteryx*, wing.)

ARTHROPODA—The phylum of invertebrates characterized by a hard, external covering of chitin, molting, and paired, jointed legs. They have been represented since the beginning of the Cambrian period, first by trilobites. Present representatives: insects, crustaceans, spiders.—Etym: Green *pod,* foot, and *arthr,* articulated.)

ARTICULATA—Synonym of arthropoda.

ASSIMILATION—The property by which living creatures convert a foreign substance to their own matter. In viruses, this property becomes their method of reproduction. In all other creatures, this property is related to food, and it is the essential, final act of nutrition.— (Etym: Latin *simil,* like.)

AUSTRALOPITHECUS—The fossil skeleton intermediate between man and monkeys found in the southern regions of Africa, dating back one to two million years. There are several species of australopithecus, rather more apelike than manlike by their structure, but one of these forms, or else a related form, the zinjanthropus made tools and appears to be an ancestor of man. Obvious intermediate group. —(Etym: Greek *pithec,* monkey.)

B

BACTERIOPHAGE—A virus group living as parasites in bacteria. It remodels bacterial matter after its own matter, making more than one hundred viruses similar to itself from one bacterium.—(Etym: Greek *phag,* eat.) In actual fact, the bacteriophage does not eat the bacterium, nor does it incorporate the bacterium into itself. It disorganizes it and remodels it after its own structure. The bacterium becomes viruses that are copies formed outside of the original bacteriophage.

BELEMNITE—A group of cephalopod mollusks, cone-shaped, with a depression at the back like the nose of a jet airplane. Because of this, the animal swims by propulsion. By expelling water forward, its body is driven backward. Squid swim this way today. Found from the Triassic period to the Cretaceous period.—(Etym: Greek *belemn,* dart, javelin.)

BIVALVE—A group of mollusks whose shell is composed of two parts called valves; a right valve and a left valve, joined together along a hinge line. Found since the Cambrian period. Present examples: cockles, mussels, oysters.

BRACHIOPODA—A phylum of animals vaguely related to worms. They have a shell composed of two pieces called valves. One valve is on the ventral side of the body, the other is on the dorsal side. Within these shells is a pair of arms bearing tentacles by which a current of water is made to bring microscopic food to the mouth. Found since the upper Pre-Cambrian period, their numbers are distinctly decreasing in nature today (less than one per cent of shell fish species).—(Etym: Greek *pod,* foot, and *brachi,* arm.)

BRYOZOA—A phylum of animals made up of minute individual animals measuring less than one millimeter. Each individual has a crown of ciliated tentacles. They live joined together in colonies. Related to worms. Found from the Lower Silurian period to the present day.—(Etym: Greek *zo,* animal, and *bry,* moss.)

C

CAMBRIAN—The first period of the Primary era, lasting from five hundred eighty million years ago to four hundred ninety million years ago. Preceded by the Pre-Cambrian period, and followed by the Silurian. The first abundant flora and fauna fossils date from the Cambrian period.—(Etym: Cambria, an ancient Welsh tribe.)

CARBONIFEROUS—The second to last period of the Primary era lasting from three hundred fifty to two hundred eighty million years ago. Preceded by the Devonian period and followed by the Permian. Numerous coal beds.—(Etym: Latin *fer,* bearing, and *carbon,* coal.)

CELL—The smallest autonomous unit of living matter. All living organisms are formed of one or several cells, linked together or separated by intercellular matter. The essential part of the cell consists of a mass of cytoplasm, generally including a nucleus, and it is surrounded by a membrane. The nucleus is still diffuse in bacteria, but is distinct in all upper creatures.—(Etym: Latin *cellul,* little loge.)

CEPHALOPODA—A group of mollusks characterized by the tentacles surrounding their head. All marine creatures. Found from the upper Cambrian period to the present day. Examples: goniatites, ceratites, ammonites, belemnites, all of which are extinct. Cuttlefish, octopuses.—(Etym: Greek *pod*, foot, and *sephal*, head.)

CERATITES—A group of cephalopod mollusks, characterized by completely folded suture lines and indented lobes. The shell is tightly coiled. Found from the Permian period to the Triassic period.—(Etym: Greek *cerat*, horn, because of the points decorating the shell.)

CHEMICAL LAMARCKISM—Modern form of Lamarckism upheld by Wintrebert, Dechambre, and Bourdier. The organism reacts to the environment by emitting hormones or other chemical mediators. These act not only on its various organs but also on its reproductive cells. Hence heredity is possible. Clever hypothesis which explains paleontological facts and large evolutions much better than the doctrine of mutation-selection.

CHITIN—A hard, impermeable substance impregnating the outer integument of the skin of arthropoda. Ex.: the May fly and the shrimp. —(Etym: Greek *chitin*, tunic.)

CHROMOSOME—One of the small bodies of which several pairs are found in the nuclei of cells. They play a fundamental role in the transmission of many hereditary characteristics.—(Etym: Greek *som*, body, and *chrom*, color, because they react strongly to coloring agents.)

CLASS—One of the categories in the hierarchy of plant and animal classifications. A phylum is composed of classes; a class is composed of orders.

COCCOLITHOPHORE—Very simple, unicellular marine organism, belonging to the flagellate group. Covered with coccoliths which are calcareous corpuscles measuring a thousandth of a millimeter. When the coccolithophore dies, the coccoliths fall to the sea floor and help form deposits there. Found since the Cambrian period.—(Etym: Greek *phor*, bearing; *lith*, stones; *cocc*, in the form of seeds.)

COELACANTH—Family of fish fossils with internal nostrils. Therefore they were capable of breathing air. The skeleton of their fins foreshadows the feet of aerial vertebrates. Because of this, they were close to one of our ancestors. Lived in the Devonian period and on into the Cretaceous. Its present descendant, the Latimeria, is a true living fossil and was discovered in the Comoro Islands about 1948.—(Etym: Greek *acanth*, spine, and *coel*, hollow.)

COLLEMBOLA—One of the two most primitive groups of insects, wingless, and the oldest insect to have appeared: found in the Devonian period. Its name is derived from its habits: the male makes a sticky ball out of his sperm, attaches it to a horizontal thread, seizes the female and thrusts it into her.—(Etym: Greek, *embol*, thrust in, and *coll*, glue.)

COLLENIA—A fixed, aquatic fossil formed from ramified columns made up of calcareous concentric envelopes. The limestone became deposited around the bodies of blue-green algae or cyanophyta. Used to form reefs in the Pre-Cambrian period. Also found in the Primary era.

COMPETITION—According to modern works, this is the principal process of the natural selection and elimination of the least suited.

CONVERGENCE—The evolution of similar characteristics in organisms of widely different ancestry. It results from the same adaptation to one and the same function or to the same environment. For example; the fins of whales and the fins of fishes.

COPY—The reproductive system of viruses: viruses live in other organic matter which they disorganize, then reorganize into about a hundred copies of their own structure. Some scientists believe that the very first living creatures reproduced in this way, which is much simpler than all the other known reproductive methods.

CORYCIUM ENIGMATICUM—One of the oldest known fossils, dating back to about one billion, four hundred million years ago. In Finland: composed of a simple sack, it may be a blue-green algae.—(Etym: Greek *coryc*, leather bag.)

CRADLE—Limited region of the globe, where a species or a larger group originated: region of origin.

CRETACEOUS—The third and final period of the Secondary era, between one hundred thirty-five and seventy million years ago. Preceded by the Jurassic and followed by the Eocene period of the Tertiary era. Toward the end of the Cretaceous, ammonites, belemnites, and a host of large reptiles became extinct.—(Etym: Latin *creta*, chalk.)

CRINOIDS—One of the seven classes of echinoderms. Their stem is formed of discs surmounted by a circlet of featherlike arms. They are marine creatures almost always attached to the sea floor or a rock, hence the name sea lily. Found from the lower Silurian period to the present day.—(Etym: Greek *crin*, lily.)

CUTIN—An impermeable substance coating the parts of plants that are exposed to the air: namely the epidermis, aerial spores, or pollen.

It does not perish as quickly as other organic matter. So it is more often preserved (spores, pollen).—(Etym: Latin *cuti,* skin.)

CYSTOID—One of the seven main classes of echinoderms, bladderlike, and covered with many irregular plates. Found only in the Primary era. Class soon extinct. Classes with more regular plates have persisted much longer, up to the present day.—(Etym: Greek *cyst,* bladder.)

D

DARWINISM—The doctrine formulated by Darwin in 1859.
1. Species are derived one from the other.
2. Natural selection eliminates the least suited.
Darwinism does not explain the appearance of the species. In 1859, this would have been risky. It still is today.

DATURA—A genus of plant from the Solanaceous family (or the night-shade family to which the potato and tobacco also belong). The flesh of the datura is in a fleshy, prickly capsule.

DEVONIAN—The middle period of the Primary era, lasting from four hundred to three hundred fifty million years ago. Preceded by the Silurian period and followed by the Carboniferous. Life sets foot on the land for the first time during this period: plants, insects, etc.—(Etym: *Devon,* county in the south of England.)

DIATOMS—A large class of unicellular algae with chlorophyll and a brown color. The cell is surrounded by a siliceous carapace made of two valves. These are so finely decorated that they must be viewed under the microscope. Dimensions: about 0.1 mm. Living in the sea or in fresh water. Found from the upper Jurassic to the present day.—(Etym: Greek *tom* cut, and *dia,* across; the name signifies the way they are divided.)

DINOSAURIA—A large order of reptile fossils found from the Triassic to the end of the Cretaceous. They have two temporal fossae. The *Gigantosaurus* was more than one hundred fifty feet long. Their brains were minute. They disappeared at the end of the Cretaceous. Why? Excessive size? Too small a brain? Competition, but from what? Mammals were still very rare at that time.—(Etym: Greek *din,* terrible, strange.)

DIPNOI—An order of fish able to breathe in air and in water, but with fins strictly of the fish type, and this distinguished them from the coelacanth. Found from the Triassic period to the present day.—(Etym: Greek *di,* two, and *pneus,* breathe.)

DROSOPHILA—Synonym for fruit fly. See under fruit fly.—Etym: Greek *phil,* loving, and *dros,* liquid, dew.)

E

ENDEMICITY—The quality that a species or a larger group have of being indigenous to a given region. Example: armadillos are endemic of South America. Numerically speaking, the endemicity or endemicity rate of a region, for a given group, is the relationship between the number of species of this group peculiar to the region and the total number of species present in this region. For example, for many groups, the endemicity of Madagascar is ninety per cent; the endemicity of England is one per cent. This is because England has often been connected with the continent, and this has allowed exchanges.

ENDEMISM—Synonym for endemicity.

EOCENE—The first period of the Tertiary era, lasting from seventy to forty million years B.C. Preceded by the Cretaceous and followed by the Oligocene. Its first part is often called Paleocene. In the Eocene, mammals multiply, and gastropoda become dominant among the shell fish.—(Etym: Greek *eo,* dawn, and *cen,* recent.)

EOCEPHALODISCUS—Ancient Silurian genus belonging to the stomochordate group. Related to vertebrates by the dorsal axis or notochord and by the respiratory slits on the side of the pharynx. Colonial animals forming crusts.

EVOLUTION—In the sense that naturalists use it: the species are derived one from the other.

EXPLOSIVE—A genus or other group, which in a given region or at a given time, is represented by an excessive number of species. This is called an evolutionary crisis. But it has not been explained. Example: the stoastoma snails of Jamaica.

EXTINCTION—Of a fossil group. It has been observed, but it has not been explained. Competition? Excessively large organs? Hormonal imbalances? We would do best to take advantage of the data on the extinction of plants and animals from the past two or three centuries. The anecdotal interest of this has been well studied, but its possible transposition to paleontology has not. Advice for the amateur investigator.

F

FAMILY—A group of related plants or animals forming a category ranking above a genus and below an order.

FISH—In natural sciences, this name is given to vertebrates with jaws and fins. Lampreys and other fish of the Agnatha class are excluded from this definition because they have no jaws.

FOLD—A convexity directed forward in the suture line of a cephalopod mollusk. In the course of time the folded suture lines of goniatites and ammonites have become more complex.

FORAMINIFERA—A large order of unicellular aquatic animals with a carapace. The giant foraminifera measure 1 cm., and even 1.8 cm., but the average is 0.1 to 1 mm. Found from the Cambrian period to the present day. There can be hundreds of them per gram of rock. One of the best groups of statistical studies. Petroleum geologists use foraminifera to identify and correlate strata when drilling wells.—(Etym: Latin *fer*, bearing, and *foramen*, hole; because the carapace is perforated with minute holes.)

FRUIT FLY—Synonym: drosophila. Extremely useful laboratory animal for studying mutations, crossbreeds, and hereditary patrimonies. Very small, inexpensive to breed, reproducing every three weeks. Their natural rate of mutation is relatively high.

G

GASTROPODA—One of the large classes of mollusks, typified by the snail. Their shell, if they have one, is a univalve shell, usually coiled. They have a single broad foot for crawling, located on the underside of the body near the stomach. They are found from the Cambrian to the present day. But they became dominant among other marine shell fish only since the beginning of the Tertiary era, when their class underwent a large explosion.—(Etym: Greek *pod*, foot, *gaster*, stomach.)

GENE—An entity concerned with the transmission of a hereditary characteristic. This may often be a detailed characteristic or a defect. They are regarded as a small part of the chromosome, and they have a nucleic acid base.—(Etym: Greek *gen*, birth, race.)

GENUS—A category of classification between family and species. Since Linnaeus, every species is designated by two Latin words: the first word is the genus name and is always capitalized. Example: *Ceratites nodosus*. Genus: *Ceratites*. Species: *nodosus*.

GEOMETRIC PROGRESSION—Example: 1, 2, 4, 8, 16, 32. . . . or: 1, 10, 100, 1000, etc. Definition: a series of elements where the elements progress by a constant factor. The factor is 2 in our first example, 10 in the second example. A geometric progression can be increasing (preceding cases) or decreasing: 32 16, 8, 4, etc. Example: radioactive disintegration occurs following a decreasing geometric progression.

GERM CELLS—In an individual, the reproductive cells and the hierarchy of cells from which they have derived by division from the egg. Is opposed to the somatic cell.—(Etym: Latin *germen*, germ.)

GIGANTOSTRACEANS—Large group of aquatic arthropod fossils. Found from the Silurian to the Permian periods. The largest measure six feet.—(Etym: Greek *ostrac*, carapace, and *gigant*, giant.)

GONIATITES—One of the groups of cephalopod mollusks, with characteristic folded suture lines and a smooth shell with hardly any sinuosities. Found from the Devonian to the Permian periods. —(Etym: Greek *goni*, angle.)

GOTLANDIAN—In France, a synonym for upper Silurian.—(Etym: Gotland Island, in the Baltic sea.)

H

HOLOGENESIS—The hypothesis that states that the same group appears simultaneously in several regions and therefore has several cradles. Does not seem to have been verified by facts.—(Etym: Greek *genese* to be born, and *holo*, whole, over the whole earth.)

I

IMMUTABILITY—One of the theories on the origin of the species. Species are not derived one from the other. They are fixed. Each was created separately and directly from inorganic matter. Is opposed to the doctrine of evolution.

INTERMEDIATE (GROUP)—Example: the *Archaeopteryx* is an intermediate between birds and reptiles, but it is more like a bird. Such creatures or groups are obviously a sign of relationship and are also supporting evidence for the theory of evolution. Series of intermediate forms: Anthropomorphic monkeys → *Kenyapithecus* (twelve million years ago) → Zinjanthropus (one million, seven hundred thousand years ago) → Paleanthropiens (Pithecantropus, etc.) → Neantherthal man → Homo sapiens (for twenty thousand years or more). See: MAMMAL.

ISOTOPE—An atom containing the same number of electrons (and therefore the same number of protons) as another atom, but with a different number of neutrons. So the different isotopes of the same element have the same chemical properties but different masses. Some can be radioactive, others are not. Example: Carbon 14 (radioactive), Carbon 13, Carbon 12 (the most abundant). —(Etym: Greek *iso,* equal, and *top,* place: same arrangement of electrons.)

J

JAMOYTIUS—The oldest known vertebrate. It dates from the upper Silurian period. It lives in water, resembles a fish, but it has neither jaws nor limbs. It swims thanks to folds in its skin.

JURASSIC—The period in the middle of the Secondary era, lasting from one hundred eighty to one hundred thirty-five million years B.C. Preceded by the Triassic and followed by the Cretaceous. Flying reptiles and birds appear in this period.

L

LAMARCKISM—The doctrine formulated by Lamarck between 1800 and 1809. 1. The environment and the function create the organ. 2. Acquired characteristics are hereditary. There are few facts today to support this second point.

LAMELLIBRANCH—Synonym for bivalve.

LATIMERIA—Present representative of the coelacanth group living in the Comoro Islands. It was believed to have been extinct since the Cretaceous period. This is a living fossil.—(Etym: Dedicated to Miss Latimer who discovered it.)

LIFE EXPECTANCY—In a population, the arithmetic mean of the ages at which individuals die. Because this definition sounds so ominous, insurance companies have preferred the words "life expectancy," which sound more attractive to the prospective client.

LINGULELLA—One of the oldest brachiopoda dating from the upper Pre-Cambrian period. A neighboring genus, the lingula still exists today. Evolution has been very slight in this group.—(Etym: Latin *lingulella,* little tongue, because of its shape.)

LOBE—In the suture line of a cephalopod mollusk, a convexity directed back. In the course of time, the lobes have become more complex in goniatites and ammonites.

LOGARITHMIC LAW—The numerical relationship between two dimensions, so that if one of the two increases in an arithmetic progression: 1, 2, 3, 4, 5 . . . etc., the other increases in a geometric progression: for example: 1, 2, 4, 8, 16, 32 . . . etc. Synonyms: constant growth rate; exponential law. Example: Variation in the number of different species in the coastal marine shell deposits in the course of the geological eras. The number doubles in approximately one hundred million years on the average. Here time is taken in an arithmetic progression. If we make the time into a decreasing logarithmic progression, we get the phenomenon of *acceleration*. See ACCELERATION.

M

MAMMAL—A class of vertebrates that characteristically nourish their young with milk and have hairy skin. The oldest and most primitive mammals (monotremes) used to lay eggs. Example in nature today: the ornithorhynchus. Then marsupials appeared and finally the subclass of placental mammals to which we belong.

In central Asia, from the Permian period onward, all the transitions between reptiles and mammals can be found. The division between the two groups can only be conventional. Judge for yourself: the most practical division is based on the ossicles of the ear!—(Etym: Latin *mamma,* breast.)

MARSUPIAL—See: MAMMAL.—(Etym: Greek then Latin *marsup,* pouch, bag.)

MICRASTER—Genus of sea urchin fossil. Used to live in the sea, especially in the Cretaceous period.—(Etym: Greek *micr,* little, and *aster,* star, because of the shape of its upper surface.)

MIOCENE—The second to last period of the Tertiary era, lasting from twenty-five to fifteen million years B.C. Preceded by the Oligocene and followed by the Pliocene. The majority of present day genera of plants and animals were already living.—(Etym: Greek *mio,* less, fewer, and *cen,* recent; fewer recent species than in the Pliocene period.)

MUTATION—A stable, sudden change of a gene, such that the changed condition is inherited by offspring cells. Example: some oxen without horns, basset sheep, etc. Most of the mutations that have been noted are either small or else unfavorable to the creature.

MUTATION SELECTION—The explanatory doctrine of evolution, opposing Lamarckism. 1. New species appear randomly by mutation. 2. Then, by natural selection, the least suited are eliminated, and the most suited survive. Criticism: It is paradoxical to explain progress and major evolutions by events and mutations when almost all of them are either meaningless or unfavorable to the creature.

N

NUMMULITE—Genus of foraminifera, now extinct, so called because they resemble coins. Characteristic of the Eocene and Oligocene. Not found before or after those periods.

O

OLIGOCENE—The second period of the Tertiary era, lasting from forty to twenty-five million years B.C. Preceded by the Eocene and followed by the Miocene periods.—(Etym: Greek *olig,* few, *cen,* recent; few species that are identical to recent species.)

ONTOGENESIS—The development of an individual from the egg to the adult. Is compared to phylogenesis.—(Etym: Greek *genes,* genesis, and *ont,* to be.)

ORDOVICIAN—Synonym for Lower Silurian.—(Etym: Ordovices, a Celtic people from northern Wales.)

ORDER—A category of classification ranking above the family and below the class.

ORNITHORHYNCHUS—(or Australian platypus). A genus of monotremes. One of the two most archaic, present-day mammals. It lays eggs and lives in Australia. See: MAMMAL.—(Etym: Greek *rhynqu,* beak, and *ornith,* bird; because of its duckbill.)

ORTHOCERAS—A genus of cephalopod mollusk with a straight shell and simple suture lines. From the Primary era.—(Etym: Greek *cer,* horn, *orth,* straight.)

ORTHOGENESIS—Evolution in a straight line, in the same direction. Example: in the elephant family, the trunk and the tusks have lengthened in the course of time.—(Etym: Greek *genes,* genesis, *orth,* straight.)

OVULE—In root and vascular plants, the swollen part of the mother plant inside of which fertilization will take place. Then, in most of these plants, the ovule becomes the seed.—(Etym: Latin *ovul,* little egg.)

P

PALUDINA—A genus of fresh-water gastropod mollusks. Throughout the ages it has shown progressive variations. (Etym: Latin *palud,* marsh.)

PARALLELISM—The evolution of similar characteristics between two creatures of different origin but close ancestry. These similarities appear gradually at the same time in both families. Example: the signs of wear in the molars of hooved mammals from different families: oxen, horses, etc.

PERMIAN—The last period of the Primary era, lasting from two hundred eighty to two hundred thirty million years B.C. Preceded by the Carboniferous and followed by the Triassic. It was marked by extensive glaciation and by a large crisis in the living world causing a decrease in the number of species found in the strata and a renewal of numerous groups.—(Etym: from the former province of Perm, Eastern Russia.)

PHYLOGENESIS—In the doctrine of evolution, the development of successive species from the same branch or phylum. These successive species are believed to have been derived one from the other. Is compared with ontogenesis. There is a certain similarity between the two.—(Etym: Greek *genes,* genesis, and *phyl,* tribe, lineage.)

PHYSIOGNOMY—General aspect. In geology: all the physical, chemical and paleontological characteristics of a rock illustrating the conditions and environment that helped in the formation of the rock, independently of the era. Example: coastal physiognomy, muddy physiognomy.

PLACENTA—In upper mammals, a tissue complex serving as the mechanical, metabolic, and endocrine connection between the adult female and the embryo during pregnancy.—(Etym: Greek then Latin *placent,* a flat cake; so called because of its structure in man.)

PLIOCENE—The most recent period of the Tertiary era, lasting from fifteen to one million years B.C. Preceded by the Miocene and followed by the Quaternary era. The climate was cooler and toward the end of the Pliocene, glaciations were beginning.—(Etym: (Greek *plio,* more, *cen,* recent; more species identical to recent species.)

PRE-CAMBRIAN—The oldest and longest of the geological eras, extending from the origin of the earth around three billion, five hundred million years B.C. or four billion years B.C. to five hundred eighty million years B.C. Followed by the Cambrian period, hence its name. Fossils are extremely rare in this period, even where the ground was and has remained favorable for their preservation.

PRIMARY—Era extending from five hundred eighty to two hundred thirty million years B.C. Preceded by the Pre-Cambrian era and followed by the Secondary era. Animals and plants were very different from animals and plants of today.

PROTOBATRACHUS—Amphibian with a rudimentary tail. Probable ancestor of our frogs. Was living two hundred million years ago in Madagascar.

PROTOCHORDATA—One of the two groups of chordata, the other being vertebrates. Characterized by the absence of a cranium and vertebrae, and having a simple, undivided cerebrum. Example: the amphioxus.—(Etym: Greek *pro,* before.)

Q

QUATERNARY—The last of the geological eras, and by far the shortest, lasting from about one million years B.C. to 4,000 years B.C. Its date of origin is not well known, and its ending date is conventional, varying according to the points of view. The Quaternary is preceded by the Tertiary, and it is followed by the historical eras. In contrast to the Tertiary era, the glacial phases are very important. The number of species identical to present-day species is about eighty per cent to ninety per cent at the beginning and one hundred per cent at the end. Only rare genera appeared in the Quaternary era, but among them there were the ox, the horse, and the elephant. The ancestors of man appeared in the Tertiary era, and then were succeeded in the Quaternary by three main species: Paleanthropians (Pithecanthropus, etc.), Neanderthal man (from fifty thousand to twenty thousand years B.C. appoximately?), Homo sapiens (from twenty-five thousand years B.C. or perhaps before).

R

REFUGE—A limited region of the globe, to which a species or a group has withdrawn, after occupying a much vaster territory. Synonym: shelter. Example: the marsupials in Australia and South and Central America. Refuges are usually isolated, distant regions.

REGRESSIVE EVOLUTION—Hypothesis formulated in 1946, no longer arousing interest. In the beginning, God created all animals, all plants, and Adam and Eve. All were immortal, so there was no fossilization. After the original sin, all became mortal, and now we begin to find fossils. Needless to say, there are no paleontological facts to corroborate these views.

REGRESSION—Evolution moving in the opposite direction to normal evolution. In particular, decrease in size; or disappearance of an organ. Example: The hind limbs of cretaceans have regressed; in the whale, they are reduced to two little bony stilettos drowned in the muscles of the body.

REPTILE—Any of a class of vertebrates characteristically having embryonic membranes or amnions and characteristically lacking features and hair. They have horny scales. In central Asia, from the Permian period onward, all the transitions between reptiles and mammals can be seen, and the division between them is purely conventional. It has been based on an anatomical detail, namely the ossicles of the ear. Reptiles had reached their greatest peak of development during the Secondary era.

RHYNIA—Region in Scotland, geologically famous, because it was here that the oldest insects (collembola) were found as well as very ancient plants with organs adapted to life in the air. All dating from the middle Devonian period.

RUDISTID—A group of attached bivalve mollusks which used to form reefs during the Secondary era. In appearance, they are easily mistaken for corals. This is a good example of convergence.

S

SEA LILY—Synonym for one of the stalked forms of crinoid.

SECONDARY—Geological era lasting from two hundred and thirty to seventy million years B.C. Preceded by the Primary era and followed by the Tertiary era. It is subdivided into the Triassic, Jurassic, and Cretaceous periods. It is the era where reptiles and ammonites reach their highest peak of development.

SHELTER—Synonym for refuge.

SILURIAN—The second period of the Primary era, lasting from four hundred ninety to four hundred million years B.C. Preceded by the Cambrian period and followed by the Devonian. Numerous graptolites and trilobites are found during this period.—(Etym: Silures, a people of Southern Wales.)

SOMATIC CELLS—In an individual, the cells of the body that become differentiated and compose the tissues and organs of that individual. They are separate from the reproductive cells (or germ cells). Some organisms have no somatic cells. Example: unicellular organisms. —(Etym: Greek *soma*, body.)

SPARTINA—A gramineous genus, a type of grass with stiff leaves. One species, Spartina Townsendi, appeared in the south of England around 1870, and has since become more widespread. It is a good example of a new species that has probably sprung from crossbreeding.

SPECIES—Cuvier's definition: A group of animals born one from the other or born of common parents, and animals which possess, in common, distinctive characteristics. So there are two criteria: resemblance and lineage. Obviously, for fossils, we must rely on resemblances.

SPORE—A reproductive body, small (1 to 100 thousandths of a millimeter, rarely more), typically unicelluar, able to be disseminated, then able to develop directly. Spores are often disseminated by the wind. —(Etym: Greek *spor,* a sowing.)

STEPPE—A vast tract of land, without forests. In a rather dry climate, with cold or cool winters. The grass is not as thick as in fields but there are countless perennial plants.

STOMA—Any of the various small openings in the impermeable, cutinized epidermis of plants, through which gaseous exchanges occur between the air and the plant.—(Etym: Greek *stomat,* mouth.)

SUTURE—In a cephalopod mollusk, the contact line between a dividing membrane and the external part of the shell. From goniatites to ammonites, the suture lines become progressively more complex.— (Etym: Latin, *sutur,* to sew, stitch.)

T

TELLIAMED—Title of Maillet's work, which appeared in 1749. It contains a very imaginative but interesting conception of the idea of evolution.—(Etym: Anagram of the author's name.)

TERTIARY—Geological era lasting from seventy to one million years B.C. Preceded by the Second and followed by the Quaternary eras. It is subdivided into the Eocene. Oligocene, Miocene, and Pliocene periods. It is the era in which mammals flourished, especially placental mammals. Gastropoda show relatively great development. An ancestor of man, the Zinjanthropus, appears right at the very end in east Africa.

TERRITORY—Region of the globe, occupied at a given time by a given group of plants or animals.

TRIASSIC—First period of the second era, lasting from two hundred and thirty to one hundred and eighty million years B.C. Preceded by the Permian and followed by the Jurassic periods. Flora and fauna are abounding in new growth. There are large deserts.—(Etym: Greek *trias,* group of three, so called because it is subdivided into three stages.)

TRILOBITE—A class of arthropoda from the Primary era. The body is characteristically divided into three parts longitudinally and three parts vertically. They lived in the water.—(Etym: Greek *tri,* three, and *lob,* lobe.)

TYRANNOSAURUS—Carnivorous reptile fossil, fifty feet high, from the secondary era.—(Etym: Grek *saur,* lizard, and *tyrann,* tyrant.)

V

VERTEBRATE—One of the two groups of chordates. Differs from the protochordates by having a cranium and vertebrae, and because the cerebrum is subdivided into five parts.

VIRUS—The simplest and smallest group of present-day living creatures: measuring 0.1 to 0.5 thousandths of a millimeter. Lives as a parasite in cells. Reproduces by disorganizing the host substance and remodeling it into copies of itself. In the smallest viruses, no nutritive exchanges occur; in the largest, there are transitions with bacteria. Viruses today help us to visualize some of the possible characteristics of the first living creatures. But all of this is conjectural and awaits further progress of our knowledge for verification.—(Etym: Latin *virus,* venom.)

VITALISM—The philosophical doctrine that living creatures are essentially different to inorganic matter. But all recent research has tended to bridge the gap separating the inorganic from the living. It even appears possible that we may soon be able to produce living creatures, a sort of virus or autonomous genes able to live and reproduce from inorganic chemical products. Then what characteristics will we have to differentiate between living organisms and inorganic matter? Only one: living organisms have a past, a history.

The aim of this book has been to portray this history and the lesson that we can learn from it.

INDEX

Index